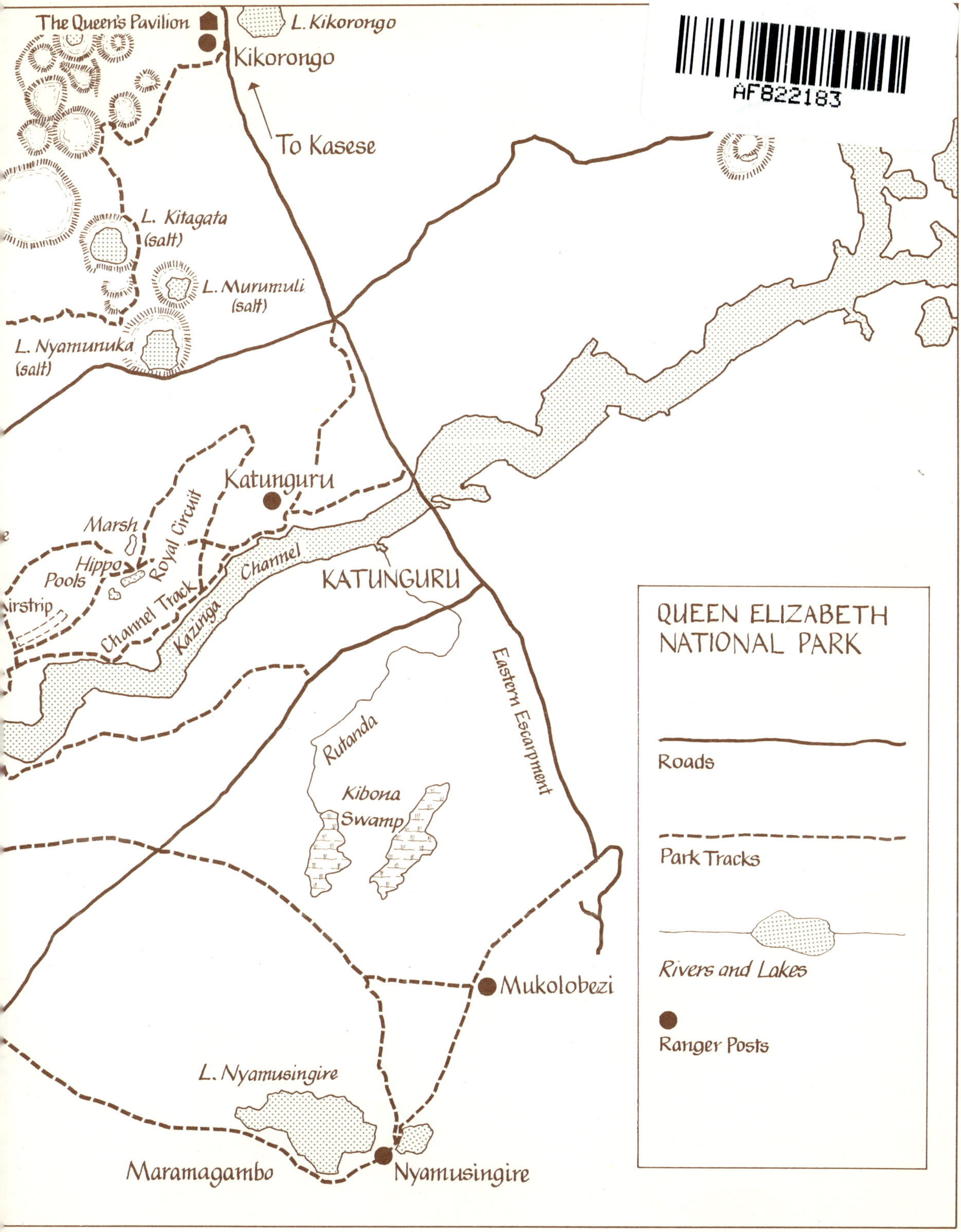

The Queen's Pavilion
L. Kikorongo
Kikorongo
To Kasese
L. Kitagata
(salt)
L. Murumuli
(salt)
L. Nyamunuka
(salt)
Katunguru
Marsh
Royal Circuit
Hippo
Pools
irstrip
Channel Track
Kazinga
Channel
KATUNGURU
Eastern Escarpment
Rutanda
Kibona
Swamp
Mukolobezi
L. Nyamusingire
Maramagambo
Nyamusingire
QUEEN ELIZABETH
NATIONAL PARK
Roads
Park Tracks
Rivers and Lakes
Ranger Posts

UGANDA QUEST

by the same author

THE BADGER

WOODLAND ECOLOGY

UGANDA QUEST

AFRICAN WILDLIFE AFTER DARK

Ernest Neal

TAPLINGER PUBLISHING COMPANY, NEW YORK

First published in the United States in 1971 by
TAPLINGER PUBLISHING CO., INC.
New York, New York

International Standard Book Number 0-8008-7923-6

Library of Congress Catalog Card Number 75-158843

Printed in Great Britain

For my wife
who shared it all
with me

Contents

Introduction 13

1. Settling in 15
2. Exploring the Savannah by Day and Night 27
3. The Attraction of Water 47
4. The Larger Carnivores 57
5. The Forest Regions 72
6. The Banded Mongoose Investigation 84
7. Inter-Relationships of the Savannah 111

Appendix
The Banded Mongoose: Summary of Data 119

Bibliography 128

List of Illustrations

1. Mweya from the air *between pages 24 & 25*
2. The old Chief Warden's house where we lived
3. Defassa Waterbuck (male)
4. Bushbuck (female)
5. Bohor Reedbuck (male)
6. Topi
7. Uganda Kob (male)
8. Genet in a Euphorbia tree (by flashlight) *between pages 40 & 41*
9. Spotted Hyaena yawning
10. Lake fish; two Tilapia and a Barbel
11. Lung fish
12. White-necked Cormorants
13. Marabou Stork
14. Yellow-billed Stork
15. Saddle-billed Storks
16. Malachite Kingfisher on Papyrus *between pages 56 & 57*
17. Lily-trotter walking on floating Nile Cabbage
18. Marabou Storks and Sacred Ibis
19. School of Hippos in the Kazinga Channel
20. Bull Hippo showing aggression
21. Grasshopper showing flash coloration when about to fly
22. A well-camouflaged Grasshopper
23. Elephant scenting *between pages 72 & 73*
24. Recognition by Bull Elephant of newly born Calf
25. Lions feeding at a Buffalo kill (by flashlight)
26. Spotted Hyaenas at the remains of a lion kill (by flashlight)

27. White-backed Vultures
28. Bull Buffalo and family of Egyptian Geese
29. Lion pride resting by Hippo Pool
30. Elephants at Hippo Pool
31. Lions resting in a Ficus tree at Ishasha *between pages 88 & 89*
32. Lion showing aggression when disturbed while courting
33. Giant Forest Hog at Ishasha
34. Rousette Fruit Bats in a cave in the Maramagambo Forest
35. Thonningia flowers from the forest floor
36. Large congregation of Olive Baboons at the edge of the Maramagambo Forest
37. A butterfly uses another as a resting place
38. The Yellow Pansy: a common forest butterfly
39. Encounter on the mountain road through the Impenetrable Forest *between pages 104 & 105*
40. View from the Ruwenzori looking west towards the Ituri Forest
41. Banded Mongoose pack on the move
42. Banded Mongoose pack
43. Banded Mongoose suckling young at the den
44. Banded Mongoose tracks in mud

All photos by the author, except No 34 which was taken by Andrew Neal.

Acknowledgments

I wish to record my warmest thanks to Dr Keith Eltringham, Director of the Nuffield Unit of Tropical Animal Ecology, for my initiation into the mysteries of Africa after dark and for invaluable help in numerous ways, and to Mrs Eltringham and all members of NUTAE for their many kindnesses. I would also like to express my gratitude to Mr Obondio Odur, Chief Warden of Queen Elizabeth National Park, and his Rangers for their co-operation and interest. I would also like to thank Betty, my wife, who shared with me both the excitements and the trials of field work under unfamiliar conditions and who helped so much to make the trip memorable. Finally I would express my thanks to the Royal Society for the financial help which made it all possible, and to the Headmaster and Council of Taunton School who gave me the necessary leave of absence.

Introduction

What is it about Africa that gets into your bones and makes you long to be back again? Few people who have spent time there would deny that there is something, but defining it is not easy.

My wife and I had previously spent six weeks in 1962 going round some of the National Parks of Kenya, Tanzania and Uganda. It had been a great experience to see some of the finest areas for wildlife on the continent. But this had just whetted our appetite for more! It had been thrilling to see, but at the same time exasperating not to be able to attempt to get to grips with it.

Five years later the chance came. I was invited by the Director of the Nuffield Unit of Tropical Animal Ecology (NUTAE for short) to come out for a spell to work with the Unit at their research headquarters in Queen Elizabeth National Park, Uganda. Nobody had done much research on any of the middle-sized carnivores; would I like to have a go?

I was in a full-time job as a schoolmaster, but here was an opportunity that was unlikely to come again. Every help was given, and just before Christmas 1968 my wife and I landed on the grassy air strip at Kasese in a Dakota of East African Airways – the start of a four-month adventure.

I was under no illusion about the difficulties of the project. In four months you could do little more than see some of the problems and with luck initiate a line of research, but if I could do that it would be well worth while as others could follow it up.

Most of the middle-sized carnivores like genets, civets, servals and some of the species of mongoose, were largely nocturnal. You were lucky if you saw them at all. How could you set about studying them?

It was almost incredible as a zoologist brought up in Britain to be told that 'almost anything you find out about them will be valuable because virtually nothing is known of their ecology.' Looking up the literature soon convinced me that this statement was correct. These species were, of course, well known, but as living animals only in zoos, or occasionally as pets. The people who knew most about them were probably those who never put pen to paper; the hunters, the trackers, and perhaps the poachers.

I had gained a lot of experience studying badgers in Britain, and as they are largely nocturnal this had given me a feeling for the night creatures, but studying their counterparts in the African bush at night could be very different!

Unfortunately the only badger in Africa is the honey badger and they were so rare in Queen Elizabeth National Park that there was no real prospect of studying them there. I was told they had been seen there on only four or five occasions during the past ten years. However, hyaenas, genets, civets and five species of mongoose were to be found in the Park, and some of these were not uncommon, although seldom seen because of their nocturnal habits. All belonged to the family *Viverridae*, a group nearly related on the one hand to the *Mustelidae* to which the badgers belong, and on the other to the *Felidae* which contains the cats.

So there was plenty of scope. Before we could get down to more detailed work it was essential for us to soak ourselves in the general ecology of the Park. We had to gain experience of the ecosystem as a whole before we could hope to see the role of the middle-sized carnivores within it. It was one thing to know something of the theory, quite another to experience it.

These explorations brought us into intimate contact with most of the larger fauna of the Park and this book tells of some of our experiences, some relevant to the main issue, some irrelevant. Many incidents which were exciting to us would be commonplace to the initiated, but they are included in the hope that others who come fresh to Africa, and especially perhaps those who visit the National Parks, will find something that will make their safaris even more rewarding.

CHAPTER ONE

Settling in

Queen Elizabeth National Park was established in 1952. It comprises an immense area of about 760 square miles in the extreme west of Uganda. It is dominated in the north-west by the magnificent range of the Ruwenzori – the Mountains of the Moon – with snow-capped peaks rising to over 16,000 feet. In the west and south-west the Park is bordered by Lake Edward and the Congo, and in the east by the escarpment of the great Western Rift Valley. In the north of the Park is Lake George, joined to Lake Edward by the twenty-mile Kazinga Channel. These lakes are about 3000 feet above sea level, so in spite of the fact that the equator runs through the Park, the climate is just pleasantly hot most of the year.

The headquarters of the Park is at Mweya, situated on a small peninsula projecting into Lake Edward at its north-east end and bounded by the westerly end of the Kazinga Channel. Mweya is strategically placed, as it is virtually cut off from the rest of the Park by a narrow neck of land, and because it is high, commands majestic views of Lake Edward, the Congo Mountains and the Ruwenzori.

Mweya consists of Park Administration buildings and Wardens' houses, a first-class safari hotel, the Nuffield Research Unit with its laboratories and staff houses, and accommodation for those employed in the Park, with a school for their children, a first-aid post, a general store or duka and a canteen.

It is impossible to get an adequate idea of the Park from a car; it is too vast and in many places quite inaccessible to motor vehicles. We were fortunate, because the Nuffield Unit possessed a light aircraft which was regularly used for game counts and this proved an admirable way of getting a bird's eye view of the whole area.

One of the current pieces of research was on pelicans, and these were counted each week from the air to see how their numbers fluctuated at different seasons. They occurred in scattered flocks wherever there was sufficient water to provide an adequate supply of fish for their needs. To count them, the plane, flying slowly at about 500 feet, had to follow the lines of the lakes and channel and virtually covered most of the major areas of vegetation in the Park.

Going on one of these counts was a most rewarding experience. Keith Eltringham, Director of NUTAE, was our pilot and Nassa Din, the Scientific Warden, did the counting. The sun shone brilliantly and the aircraft's shadow looked like some gigantic bird of prey as it glided over the vegetation below.

We flew south-east from the Mweya air strip on the peninsula towards the Rift Escarpment, passing low over the bushy savannah, mainly green grass dotted with thicket clumps. Game tracks criss-crossed the landscape, and wherever there was standing water they converged like roads at a junction. We saw family parties of elephants, larger concentrations of buffalo and smaller groups of waterbuck and other antelope.

As we approached the escarpment the landscape became more wooded and turning south we saw ahead of us the vast tract of forest known as the Maramagambo. We were heading for some lakes within the forest which were large enough to support some pelican colonies.

If the colonies were small enough you could count the birds accurately as you flew by, but the large ones had to be photographed and the numbers determined later.

The forest region was fascinating to see from above, the tree canopies fitting into each other like a mosaic of various shades of green, forming a carpet which stretched far into the distance.

The escarpment greatly increases the annual rainfall and allows the growth of these magnificent trees in the country nearby. We saw clearings in the forest where it was particularly damp, and here there were concentrations of buffalo and elephant.

Flying more to the south-west we saw the forest gradually change through thicket to open grassy savannah with scattered trees giving it a park-like appearance. This was the Ishasha region where large herds of topi and kob could be seen.

We turned back at the River Ishasha which marks the Congo border and followed the marshy edge of Lake Edward northwards. There were a number of pelican colonies along this coastal region, especially where rivers from the escarpment and the Maramagambo opened into the lake.

Back over Mweya again we followed the line of the Kazinga Channel towards Lake George. The schools of hippos along the Channel looked like groups of grey slugs as we passed over them. Some were basking, but the majority were half submerged in the shallow water.

To the north of Lake George there were vast areas of papyrus swamp looking deceptively solid from above and as we followed the edge of the lake we saw a poacher's hide-out among the reeds. It was so easy to spot from the air, but would have been completely invisible from land level and extremely difficult to reach. Keith Eltringham turned the plane and dived low over it to scare the poachers if they were there; it would at least warn them that they had been discovered.

To the north-east of Lake George the Mpango river came into sight as it flowed into the lake. Following it up a few miles, we saw where its waters flowed mightily over the Beaton Falls, its banks clothed in riparian forest. One area was particularly interesting because of its concentration of palm-like cycads, a group of plants belonging to a most ancient class of conifers, relics of a flora more characteristic of past ages.

Going farther north we surveyed an area south of Kasese where pelicans were breeding in the trees. Here we had magnificent views of the deep blue line of the Ruwenzori.

We had now covered most of the Park as far as habitats for pelicans were concerned, but there was still one region west of Mweya round Katwe to the Congo border which had not been covered. It was here that we passed over the famous salt lake at Katwe which appeared blood red from above. There was more luxuriant riparian forest near the mouth of the Nyamugasani river and beyond it some bushy savannah with fine acacia trees nearer to the Congo end.

Returning inland behind Katwe fishing village we saw to the north the crater area of the Park. This is pock-marked with many craters of volcanic origin said to be only about seven thousand years old. Some of the craters had water in them, others were dry, some had wooded slopes, others grassy; very different country from any other part of the Park.

We returned to Mweya after about two and a half hours' flying, passing low over the air strip once to scare off the waterbuck before coming in to land. It had given us a much better idea of the immensity of the region and the great variety of habitats. The tiny tracks spiderwebbing over the Park emphasized the enormous areas where no tracks existed and the relative inaccessibility of much of the region. The Maramagambo forest itself has so far only been partly investigated;

from the air it had appeared so possible – on foot it would be a very different matter.

Betty and I were to live in the old Chief Warden's house, an attractive African-style building overlooking the flatter region of the peninsula. It had recently been vacated when the Chief Warden, Obondio Odur, had moved into a new house next door.

It was the last of the old houses and was sturdily constructed of mkindu palm logs with cement between and with a fine thatched roof of papyrus reed. It had been built for Rennie Bere when he was Chief Warden of the Uganda Parks, and we felt very honoured when we heard that H.M. Queen Elizabeth the Queen Mother had stayed there when she had visited the Park in 1959. There was still a canopy in the bedroom. Whether this had been put up for the Queen Mother's benefit originally or for the previous owners we did not enquire, but there was no doubt that it served a useful purpose, as the thatch above contained a most varied fauna which periodically lost its footing!

The thatch kept the house remarkably cool by day and in this respect was far more efficient than more modern materials. The temperature inside seldom rose above 85°F., and incidentally never dropped below 70°.

Our first few days were full of new sensations, new experiences; our nights were too! Even going to bed had its surprises.

We became very familiar with the fauna of the house. The large cockroach (*Periplaneta americana*), beloved of examiners in zoology courses, scuttled in all directions when the light was put on. We were philosophically tolerant of their attentions at first, but when one woke me up by crawling over my face my attitude rapidly changed and we started a minor war. We found the exact location of the beds in relation to the canopy and walls was strategically important.

Identification of the fauna by sound after the lights had been put out was problematical and often inaccurate, but loud gnawings and scrapings coming from one of the cupboards turned out to be the sign of the African dormouse; a charming creature to have as a bedroom companion.

Constant ticking noises, punctuated at intervals by what sounded like falling plaster, turned out to be termites at work. They seemed to be steadily taking the place to bits! Some hardboard covering was being rapidly removed and major action had to be taken to curtail their activities. Although the house had been built on concrete foundations, it only took a crack to let the termites through and they were certainly making the best of their opportunities.

We heard many rustlings in the thatch; some, no doubt, were made by small rodents, but others were made by larger creatures. It was not long before we saw one of them face to face: a two foot monitor lizard. Periodically it would leave its home in the thatch and explore the outside drainage system of the house, but if somebody appeared it would rapidly retreat to safety.

But not all the noises came from inside the house. It was marvellous to be awake listening to the weird contact calls of the hyaenas and the grunts and snorts of the hippos when they left the water to graze on the slopes in front of the house. We were woken up one night by a strange sniffing noise which seemed to be coming from the region of the window. Jumping out of bed to investigate, we looked up at the moving shape of a massive elephant. It had been sniffing through the window, no doubt to discover who were the new arrivals. It was in no hurry to depart, and as we watched it from two yards away it took a large mouthful of white flowers from the border outside before taking a leisurely leave.

During our first few days we were initiated into the everyday routine of the Unit, and Keith took us out on various projects, showing us the main areas near Mweya. It was essential to get the feel of the place and find out what could and could not be done, get used to the Land-Rover and formulate plans for finding the middle-sized carnivores.

We looked forward with keen anticipation to our first night expedition. It was one thing to see the game by day, but at night it would be far more thrilling.

Keith had been carrying out weekly hare counts after dark and one of these trips provided us with our first opportunity of experiencing wild Africa at night.

After supper on our third day we boarded the short wheel-base Land-Rover, carrying a powerful hand-held spotlight which could be run off the car battery, and a small tape recorder to help with the counting. Our objective was the old air strip several miles from Mweya. It had not been used since the strip on the peninsula had been made and it had become a favourite haunt for grazing animals. As the area was well defined and easily accessible, it was a good place for regular counts so that numbers could be compared over the years. The technique was to zigzag the area methodically so as to cover the whole strip, moving the spotlight from side to side and looking for eye reflections as we went. Although the grass was tall at this season it was not too difficult to pick them out. Caught in the beam you could see the hares were smaller than the European species, with shorter ears, but otherwise they looked very similar.

Slowly we combed the area, counting the hares as we went. Beyond the headlamps and the moving spotlight all was blackness. Suddenly a great grey shape loomed up ahead and we took avoiding action – an elephant! We kept it in the spotlight in case it should take an interest in us, but it placidly went on feeding. We saw several others further on, including cows with calves, but as the terrain was flat there was no difficulty in avoiding them.

It was no easy matter quartering the area in the dark to cover each part of it, especially with elephants scattered about as unpredictable hazards, but Keith knew the place well and there were no snags. As the vehicle nosed its way through the long grass quail got up at intervals, hovering like giant moths in the headlights before flying on and flopping down into the grass again. Two pairs of eyes, large and golden, reflected our beam as it stabbed the darkness on one side; we got nearer and a pair of bushbuck leapt away – lovely creatures with spots on their flanks. They soon disappeared into the darkness.

As we neared the end of the strip we saw a line of eyes all turned in our direction. As the beam swept from left to right it picked up more and more reflections, which looked like lights on the promenade at Brighton, there were so many of them! It was a herd of buffalo, each animal facing our way!

We left the air strip and carefully made our way along a rough track which led towards Hippo Pool. Excitement was in the air and we wondered what we should see next. We hadn't long to wait: from behind a dense clump of bushes came an enormous hippo which stopped on the track in front of us staring uneasily at our headlights. We stopped and waited. We could just see two others, their eyes just catching the reflections of the lights. The first one stood its ground, giving us a nasty look which was difficult to interpret.

From a distance of a few yards it was ugliness personified, its skin glistening with sweat and resembling the colour of raw meat. Keith just waited: then with surprising speed it made off like a huge pinkish-brown cylinder motivated by short fast-moving legs: the other two followed after.

We spent the rest of the trip looking for any animals that could be found and hoping to pick up the eye reflections of one of the smaller carnivores. A single eye, red in colour, shone back at us at ground level. We slowly approached. At three yards it still had not moved. At last we saw what it was, still as a stone and flat on the ground – a nightjar! We could see every detail of its beautifully camouflaged plumage.

On again, we followed the open spaces between dense clumps of bushes. Two very bright eyes, golden and close together, stared unwinkingly back at us. We turned towards it to get a better view but it shot away before we had time to see it properly. It was running low to the ground and had a very long tail: was it a mongoose or a genet? We increased our speed over the rough ground trying to get a better view as it snaked its way through the vegetation trying to avoid our beam. We got closer and it dashed across a more open patch and at last we could see it properly. The long ringed tail, longer than the body, gave it away: it was a genet. There was no point in following it farther so we slowed down to let it get away and it disappeared into some bushes. This was very exciting; we had seen the first of our carnivores!

We were now not far from Hippo Pool and having made a note of where we had seen the genet for a possible follow-up another day, we slowly approached the pool. Here the ground was completely bare of vegetation as the hippos had long since grazed it away. There were several of these great animals near the water, the eyes of others still in the pool shone back at us. We kept a wary eye open for any running in our direction as any disturbance tends to make them run back to the water. The bother is that they don't look where they are going when frightened or dazzled by the lights and they can weigh over two tons!

More eyes ahead of us, this time rather higher off the ground – four pairs near together. Getting nearer we could pick out their outlines – rounded ears and sloping backs – hyaenas! We stopped, switched off the engine and waited. They sat and stared at us, eyes glowing brightly. Moving the beam all round us we counted eight. They were unafraid and very curious, watching us from a distance of about twenty yards. What were they waiting for?

We returned to Mweya by the Royal Circuit. Many more nightjars were squatting on the track, taking off at the very last moment just as it seemed a collision was inevitable.

Just round a bend an elephant was in the middle of the road: it had a calf beside it. Keith jammed on the brakes. The elephant hardly deigned to look in our direction but continued to feed on some vegetation on the verge. We waited. It kept on feeding, choosing each tuft of grass with what seemed to us unnecessary care. We were not far from the notice which read: 'Elephants have right of way'! There was no doubt that this one had and knew it, and nobody was going to hurry it. At long last it tossed its trunk to one side and sauntered off with its calf and we were able to proceed.

We saw no more carnivores that night, but the trip had been a thrilling initiation into the technique of finding and coping with the animals at night. From now on it was up to us!

The next day was Christmas Eve. While most of the community were directing their attention towards the Fancy Dress Party at the hotel that evening, we were able to do a trip round the peninsula with Keith. This was a possible area for studying the middle-sized carnivores, as it was isolated from the rest of the Park, being almost completely surrounded by water. Most of it was inaccessible to visitors and was looked upon as a research area. A number of long term projects were being carried out there, and there was so much data already collected that if we could study our carnivores there it would fit in very well.

At one time the peninsula had been heavily overgrazed by hippos and suffered severe erosion as a result. Many of the other game had left the area as there was not enough food for their requirements. It was decided that the only answer was to cull all the hippos in that region to restore the balance. The results had been spectacular. The vegetation had recovered rapidly and the game had come back. To study these changes, game counts of the whole area were carried out each week. Counts were first made by plane and then later in the day another one was made by Land-Rover to increase the accuracy. This had been going on for several years and the data acquired gave an interesting picture of the changes in game numbers both as a result of the culling and as a seasonal phenomenon.

We were most anxious to explore the area and assess its possibilities. The going was not easy as we bumped along, avoiding the worst of the muddy wallows. We put up four bull buffalo all covered with oozy mud. They lumbered off to find a peaceful mud bath elsewhere.

Marabou storks were standing like statues by a muddy inlet of the lake, looking unwashed and dishevelled beside some immaculate pelicans. A goliath heron, the tallest of all the herons with a height of about four feet, stood at the lake's edge intently watching the water for an approaching fish. A group of hadada ibis with metallic green gloss on their dark wings and characteristic curved bill, took to flight with a raucous volley of protest, settling a few hundred yards farther on to continue their feeding undisturbed.

There were many wart-hogs on the peninsula. We saw them as small family parties in the open areas between the clumps of bushes. They have great character and look at you when you approach with alert attention before swinging round and trotting off at a pace, tails held erect like pennants in the breeze. When seen head on you can easily distinguish the sexes as the males have an extra pair of warts on their faces and their vicious looking tusks are usually much bigger.

Wart-hogs are good diggers, excavating large holes in which they shelter for the night, their heads facing outwards in the best defensive position. Gerald Clough, who was doing research on wart-hogs, used to visit all the holes over a selected area each day. He tied black cotton over each hole to see which was being used. He found that wart-hogs were distinctly territorial, each group having bolt holes to dive into if alarmed. Some holes only went in a few feet, others up to sixteen feet. The animals always went in backwards if there was no room for turning round, otherwise they went in the usual way.

Wart-hog holes are some of the chief hazards when using a vehicle over rough country as the long grass often hides their position. If you get a wheel stuck in one it's not always easy to get out. We were told the best technique was to raise the wheel out of the hole with the long jack, place the spare wheel in the hole, lower the wheel on to it and drive on, remembering to pick up the spare wheel before you went! We had to remind ourselves that you couldn't just phone up the nearest garage if you got stuck; it was very much up to you!

We saw our first banded mongoose that morning. They seemed to appear from nowhere and were all around us, darting to and fro in the long grass and standing up momentarily to get a view of us before dashing off again. There must have been quite ten of them – dark brown with conspicuous banding in the hind region of the body. This species was the only strictly diurnal mongoose in the Park and one that we hoped to study in more detail.

Looking straight ahead of us through binoculars we saw a single lioness, yellowish brown against the greener grass. She was moving quickly and purposefully and we wondered what she was up to. In the heat of the day most lions are as a rule sleeping it off in the shade of some bushes. Perhaps she was particularly hungry, being away from the main pride; or had she got cubs somewhere? We could not follow her movements for long, but she was still on her own a few days later when we saw her running along the bottom of our garden while we were sitting on the verandah. She was certainly using the peninsula as a hunting ground on her own.

Reaching some higher ground we were able to get good views of most of the peninsula. In one region the thicket was much closer and there were more euphorbia trees; some elephants were browsing there. Two fish eagles were perched on the top of one of the euphorbias: they periodically twisted their heads backwards and forwards as they let out their wild trumpeting cries.

A large herd of buffalo was massed by the edge of the lake near the point where the Kazinga Channel flowed into it. They showed much variation in coat colour. The majority was the usual dark colour, but some were much lighter and more reddish. The latter are more characteristic of buffalo from the Congo.

Our trip had been a useful introduction to the peninsula area which clearly showed possibilities, but we felt that the opportunities here were very limited for night work, as the terrain was very difficult with so many wallows and wart-hog holes. Progress by Land-Rover would be very slow at night and in places almost impossible. By day, it was ideal in many ways and might be an excellent place to study banded mongooses if they habitually used the area. It was best to keep an open mind for the present.

The party that night at the hotel was an interesting diversion from carnivores. A chorus of schoolgirls sang familiar Christmas carols as we dined on the terrace on barbecued wart-hog steaks, among other delicacies. The fancy-dress competition was judged, there was dancing in the lounge and in no time it was midnight and Christmas Day upon us.

It was a wonderful night, warm and still, with the landscape dimly lit by the distant stars and a full moon directly overhead. It was incongruous to stand there on the edge of the terrace. Behind us was the noise of talking, music and dancing; in front, dimly visible, was wild Africa, with the lake far below sparkling in the light of the moon; and at that very moment men were circling it in Apollo 8 in preparation for a landing within a few months.

Christmas morning! It was not the weather for turkey and plum pudding! There was a heat haze which effectively blotted out the Ruwenzori as we sat on the verandah scanning the peninsula below us for game. A group of elephant was drinking at the water's edge and the

1. Mweya from the air

2. The old Chief Warden's house where we lived

3. Defassa waterbuck (male)

4. Bushbuck (female)

5. Bohor reedbuck (male)

6. Topi

7. Uganda kob (male)

herd of buffalo we had seen the day before had moved over in the night and were slowly grazing their way towards the point.

There was a bird bath just in front of the house which was filled each morning, and beside it a deep stone trough. We wondered what the trough was for, as the birds could not reach the water; it seemed rather pointless filling it with water each day. But of course we hadn't realized that this provided free drinks for hyaenas or elephants which happened to visit our unfenced garden at night. Later, we learned to recognize the lapping noises when hyaenas were making their rounds.

The birds were a joy to watch as we rested. Many species visited the bird bath and identification was not difficult. This was arm-chair ornithology at its best.

There was a large colony of black-headed weavers at the back of the house, which was in a state of continuous activity. Many of them came and bathed in front of us, displaying the gorgeous yellow of their plumage.

Tiny fire finches usually came in pairs. Every action was carried out precisely and was usually immediately copied by the other; tidy little deep-red males and more sombre greyish females.

Bronze mannikins, like diminutive sparrows, busily searched for seeds on the lawn with a quick visit to the bath every now and then for a drink to wash them down.

Grey-headed sparrows were nesting under the eaves and their incessant chirpings were a reminder of the house sparrows at home; but it was the grey-headed kingfisher that really excited us as it flew to one of the posts. Seen from in front, it was a comparatively sombre bird, but when it flew, the electric blue of its wings was a magnificent sight. It was feeding on insects in the manner of a flycatcher, repeatedly returning to a convenient perch after each short sortie. It was queer to think of a kingfisher as an insectivorous bird.

The most brilliant bird to come to the bath was a red bishop, one of the most striking black and red birds we saw – they are allied to the weavers. African pied and yellow wagtails searched for insects on the lawn and were joined by a flock of seedeaters. Among these were some pin-tailed whydahs; the black and white cocks had tremendously long tails which trailed along the ground while they were feeding.

Our next visitor was a white-browed robin chat, a beautiful relation of the blackbird with bright orange rufous underparts and a conspicuous white eye stripe.

We discovered that a lizard had its house under the bird bath. With jerky movements and long pauses it climbed up to get a drink before rushing back to cover again.

From over to our left a large male waterbuck approached the garden. There was nothing to disturb it and it came closer and closer; a magnificent creature with long ringed horns which curved slightly forwards and a grey-brown, shaggy coat. Later we got to know this animal well, as it claimed our garden as part of its territory.

Mosque swallows kept flying under the eaves above our heads inspecting the place for a possible nesting site. Their pleasant honking sounded like notes from a toy horn.

Over the rough grass beyond the lawn a flappet lark was making a noise like a rattle. It made this peculiar noise as it rose in the air by snapping its wings together. It was a form of display. The variety of birds seemed endless as we lazed away the hot afternoon.

It was all very peaceful!

There was a thunderstorm early that evening and as we waited for it to clear before going off we watched the reactions of the birds to the storm. Quite a number of marabous had collected on the lawn; they stood like statues facing the wind. They looked like soldiers trying to stand at attention for long periods during an inspection. It was their heavy bills that were the problem. Slowly, as we watched, they would sag lower and lower until they reached an angle when a reflex would cause them to bring them up with a jerk again.

When the rain stopped they all started to stalk forward, peering for insects in the grass that had been disturbed by the rain.

Before the rain came a large group of vultures had been attacking the last remains of a carcass just over the rim of the slope. The rain was the signal to stop pecking at bones which no longer had any flesh on them. They stood around, bedraggled and all hunched up waiting for it to stop. When it did clear and the sun came out they flew into the euphorbias and stretched out their wings like umbrellas to dry, reminiscent of cormorants after diving.

An hour later the tracks were dry enough for driving; it was time for a further exploration.

CHAPTER TWO

Exploring the Savannah by Day and Night

It was now very much up to us. What should our policy be? Obviously the first thing was to get to know the geography of the region round Mweya as well as possible both by night and day and find as many of the middle-sized carnivores as we could. It was far better to know one region well rather than to search too far afield. The nearer it was to Mweya the less time and petrol we should waste getting there, so we decided to concentrate for the first few weeks on the region roughly enclosed by tracks known as the Royal Circuit and including the attractive country bordering the Kazinga Channel. Occasionally we extended our search towards the main gate on the one hand and Katunguru on the other. It looked a promising area of savannah and included Hippo Pool and a large marshy area to the north-west of it which at one time had been a large hippo wallow.

It was our intention to mark on a map the position of each carnivore we saw, so that in the end a pattern might emerge which would help us to understand their distribution. It might then be possible to correlate distribution with the type of vegetation in the area and find what their preferences were.

By tying white markers to trees or bushes where we had seen a carnivore by night we would have places where we could search in the daytime for possible dens or hide-outs where they might be living. It was obviously of great importance to find out where these animals lived. If they were on the move all the time the position was nearly hopeless, but if they were breeding and we found the den, then this would give us a focal point for systematic watching and that might get us somewhere.

It was possible that some of these carnivores used wart-hog holes as dens either for breeding or hiding up during the day. Careful tracking might show if these were occupied, and subsequent watching at dusk would be well worth trying. We just had to try anything and see what luck came our way. Our night excursions were always exciting, even if we discovered very little. There was always that feeling of expectancy and uncertainty which kept you keyed up; adventure could always be round the corner and sometimes it was! Africa after dark was so different from its sunny counterpart; you felt the immensity of the country more strongly, its mystery more vividly; it kept you on the alert all the time.

One evening, a few days after Christmas, we set off soon after dark. A recent thunder shower had made the track slippery, but as long as you kept to the top of the murram the Land-Rover behaved quite well. Hares were particularly abundant that night: we counted twenty-seven during the first three miles. Perhaps the rain had brought them out of the grass on to the drier track in greater numbers than usual. Nightjars, too, were squatting on the ground every hundred yards or so. They were Gaboon nightjars, not unlike the British species, but with more white on the wings and with a shorter tail.

Rounding a corner the headlights picked up what looked at first to be a greyish cat sitting upright on the track. To our surprise, on closer inspection it turned out to be a very large owl with prominent ear tufts. It was a Verreaux's eagle owl, one of the largest of the African owls.

We kept seeing tiny frogs jumping on the track in front of the car. In spite of their small size they jumped prodigious heights, certainly several feet into the air.

It was extremely dark as there was no moon and we found we had arrived at Hippo Pool almost without warning. Judging by the eye reflections, there were still many hippos in the water. In fact, whenever we passed the pool at night we always found at least a fifth of the population had not left. Either they leave at different times and for varying periods, so that there are always a good many there, or, being grazers which feed only on land, the food can last them more than the twenty-four hours. This would not be surprising as a hippo will eat as much as one hundred pounds of grass during the night.

We slowly moved along the edge of the water, carefully avoiding the hippos which had come on land. Egyptian geese were standing in the shallows and our approach caused them to stir uneasily.

We had some difficulty in finding the track towards the marshy area; the range of headlights and spotlight was very limited and if anything they accentuated the darkness all around us. We could see no landmarks, and we realized how easily we could get lost at night once we left the tracks. Even when there was a moon, much of the country looked similar and if lost you had to set a route by compass, knowing that if you kept a straight course you would eventually reach one of the main tracks if you didn't get bogged down or run into a wart-hog hole.

We found the track at last and just before we reached the marshy area we saw two eyes ahead of the right size and distance apart to be of special interest to us. We approached slowly and saw a beautiful civet. It stood and faced the headlights and we saw every detail before it ambled off into the grass. It was the first civet we had seen. Spotted rather like a genet, it was larger and stood much higher off the ground; the tail was ringed but was relatively much shorter than a genet's.

A few hundred yards farther on we knew we had arrived near the marshy area because the frogs and toads were making such a din. Leaving the track, we went as near as we could to the marsh without getting bogged down and turned the engine off to listen. The noise was almost deafening. At least three species were present judging by the distinctive noises. We could see the toads in the spotlight as they sat in the shallow water with their heads exposed and their vocal sacs extended on either side of the throat as big as ping-pong balls. Bull frogs of great size croaked in the background and a smaller frog with pointed snout and a broad green line down the back was there too in large numbers. We made a tape recording before returning to the track.

On the way back to Mweya that night the engine began to splutter and then died on us completely. There was plenty of petrol, but when the starter was tried it had that exasperating finality about its response so well known to those not mechanically minded. Not a splutter! We left it to cool down and tried again. Still no response!

No other vehicle was likely to come our way until morning, and walking the two miles home was not a good idea. There was nothing for it but to find the cause. Plugs were removed and cleaned, carburettor examined and petrol pipes blown through with great determination and periodic flashes of hope, but the starter still made its unresponsive noises. After about two hours I had done everything I could, so we prepared for an uncomfortable night. There were compensations. The moon was now up and it was a lovely night; something interesting might turn up. By way of saying good night I tried the starter once more, and the engine started!

We decided to get back as quickly as possible, in case the engine became temperamental again. This was a mistake, as round the first bend there were three hippos lying down on the verge. We had no time to brake and passed within a couple of yards of them before they had time to get up. I don't know who was the more surprised, but we learnt our lesson! There were no further mishaps and we got back home to find some hyaenas having a party at the end of the garden on some skin and bones that had previously been thrown out by one of the wardens.

We went out most nights, and it was not long before we could recognize most of the animals we met by their eye reflections. The main points of difference were the colour, their relative size, their distance apart, the height from the ground, whether you saw one at a time or always two and the pattern the eyes made when the animal moved, either keeping horizontal or gently moving up and down.

Hippos' eyes reflected red, they were small and placed wide apart and were rather high up. If the eyes were at first-storey height and rather small, and either single or very wide apart, they obviously belonged to an elephant; but you had to remember that some of the smaller animals could climb.

Buffalo eyes were relatively large, fairly high off the ground and were greenish. They were usually in large numbers of pairs, as the herds kept together at night and they all faced you. The eyes of lions reflected a golden colour like most of the cats. The antelopes were all rather similar – large eyes reflecting an almost white light. You saw them in pairs when they looked at you, but usually only one when they moved because they seldom came towards you. As they moved they went gently up and down with the movement of the neck. If they belonged to a single animal it was probably a bushbuck, if five or more they were more likely to be waterbuck.

Hyaenas' eyes shone very brightly, almost white; they were near together and rather large and a few feet from the ground. Almost invariably you saw the eyes in pairs as the animals were watching you closely.

Civets, genets and mongooses were very similar, but their eyes all appeared to be large for animals so near the ground. Genets kept their heads within an inch or two of the ground, civets about a foot above. We did not find it possible to distinguish these smaller species with certainty and always had to go nearer to be sure, but it saved a lot of time by recognizing the others, as they could usually be ignored.

Some of our encounters with the middle-sized carnivores were particularly interesting. One night we picked up the eyes of a serval near the old air strip as it crossed the track. We were able to approach very near without disturbing it, so we switched off the engine and headlights and used the spotlight only, carefully keeping the beam off the animal's eyes. It came towards us; a most beautiful creature. The big oval ears were most impressive, setting off the alert cat-like face with its dark V mark showing clearly when it looked at you. It was very much larger than a domestic cat, standing about twenty inches at the shoulder, with rather long legs. The colour was tawny yellow prominently spotted with black, the spots tending to merge into lines in the neck region. The tail was ringed, but quite short compared with civet and genet.

It moved into the long grass with great stealth, its head turning from side to side as it searched for prey. It appeared to be using its great ears far more than sight and scent. Each ear moved independently like a radar scanner ready to pick up the slightest sound. Every time it took a step it lifted its hind legs high and each foot was placed with great care and precision.

Then we caught sight of a hare, quietly feeding about fifteen feet farther on from the serval. From our high position we could see both animals clearly, but it would have been quite impossible for the serval to have seen the hare from ground level.

The hare moved a few paces at a time and then stayed still feeding, but the serval heard the movment. Immediately it bent low and started to stalk, its ears moving to get the exact position of the slightest sound from the hare. We watched, tensed up, to see the outcome. When it got to within about ten feet from the hare it stopped, the hare moved a step and the serval sprang high in the air in a great arc and landed just short of its prey which leapt away. The serval made no attempt to follow it, but continued its stealthy movements searching for another.

I was convinced it judged both distance and direction by means of its ears. No doubt it continued its slow hunting technique throughout the night until it caught something; hares or ground roosting birds like plovers or spurfowl were probably its main prey.

We saw servals on several other occasions, each time in the long grass where sight was of less importance than hearing, and always the slow, deliberate and stealthy movements were most characteristic.

Genets hunted in a very different way. One night we were slowly making our way parallel to the water's edge by Hippo Pool, scanning each clump of bushes, when we picked one up by its reflections. For once it was quite unconcerned by our presence, perhaps because it was engrossed in its hunting. It was carefully exploring a line of bushes, head near the ground, scenting all the time. It wandered in and out as if following some scent trail, but unfortunately, although we watched it for fifteen minutes we never saw it catch anything. There was always a lot of roosting birds near the pool and probably rodents too among the bushes.

The same night, half a mile farther on, we saw another genet. At first we couldn't recognize it at all, although we could see it well in the beam. It was completely black, but its tail gave it away as this was distinctly longer than the body. It was indeed a genet. Melanistic forms of several of these viverrids and cats occur occasionally, but this was the only one we saw.

This happened to be one of our more interesting night trips, because we also had excellent views of a civet. We saw the eyes a long way from the track but approached it across the rough. Our approach was inevitably rather noisy and it shot into a thick clump of bushes. We stopped about ten yards from where we had seen it disappear, turned off the engine and waited hopefully. It was not long before it re-emerged, this time taking little notice of us. Its movements were not nearly so stealthy as a serval's, and unlike the genet it kept its head high, scenting and listening as it went in and out of the bushes.

It was gradually making its way towards a wetter area covered by the wide-leaved sword grass (*Imperata*). We guessed it would be too wet to follow it, so just as it was disappearing I leant out of the window and made squeaky noises with my mouth against the back of my hand. It pricked up its ears at once and listened intently; then it came trotting across. When it was level with the front wheel it smelt it carefully and then slowly went off. It showed no fear or suspicion although I was leaning out of the near window watching it.

We saw civets on a number of occasions, the sightings being mainly by Hippo Pool and near to human habitation. There was a pair seen regularly around the house at Mweya, and once we saw one near the end of our verandah after returning late at night. This distribution of sightings strongly suggested that they made good use of carrion and scraps. A good many things died in the vicinity of Hippo Pool for one reason or another, so it was a good place for a scavenger, and there was little doubt that they got many scraps from the dustbins at Mweya if the elephants had not got there first and emptied the bins.

We examined civet dung on several occasions to shed some light on their diet. They have special 'civetries' which they use each night, where piles of dung are scattered over three or four square yards. Two of these were near Mweya. Apart from the softer food which had been almost completely digested we found many remains of the large millipedes and plenty of beetles, including the very large scarabs. So it is probable that civets are very much opportunist feeders.

We saw all the five species of mongoose which occurred in the Park, but the most strictly nocturnal species was undoubtedly the white-tailed. Early on in our explorations we followed one of these over rough country near Hippo Pool. At first we could not tell what it was as it was partly hidden by the long grass, but on passing a bare patch we saw it clearly. Every time we got near to it, it jumped high in the air, twisting its long furry white tail as it did so. This gave it a most extraordinary appearance and made it look much bigger than it actually was. This pattern of behaviour may be of use to it when pursued by a predator.

A pair of white-tailed mongooses were often seen near the hyaena den above the Kazinga Channel, but although we combed the area for a possible den we never located it. There were some deep erosion gulleys nearby and many old hyaena workings, so they may well have been using one of these.

Like the civets, the white-tails were also seen around the houses at Mweya quite frequently; they made use of any available scraps and were a potential danger to poultry. More typically they are said to feed on roosting birds and small mammals, especially rodents, hares, small reptiles, frogs and the larger insects.

The next most nocturnal mongoose we came across was the marsh or water mongoose. We only identified one animal with certainty. It was just before midnight on the drying mud of the marsh after a period of drought. We got near enough to see its uniformly dark fur and typical mongoose shape before it quickly ran to the bushy region beyond and disappeared. It looked rather like a small otter except for the tail, which was not very long and distinctly tapering.

The other mongoose species, great grey and black-tipped (slender), were seen more often during the day, although both kinds were sighted after dark as well. The banded mongoose was strictly diurnal and will be the subject of another chapter.

Every sighting of one of these middle-sized carnivores by night gave us a chance to explore the same area by day. We worked outwards from the point where it had been seen, exploring each clump of bushes and looking for any holes which could possibly house them. Each clump usually had an old termite mound as its core, but usually there was no sign of any holes in them.

We also searched for dung which might give us a clue to their whereabouts and occasionally found traces which showed that they had been about, but we found no sign of a den.

If they were not breeding, it was possible that some species which could climb well, like genets for instance, would rest during the day in trees, so we hopefully examined each euphorbia we came to, looking for the animals among their seemingly inhospitable branches; but no sign at all. It seemed that either these carnivores sheltered in dense clumps of bushes by day, and not necessarily the same ones each time, or else they were using wart-hog holes. We came across large numbers of the latter, especially in the country bordering the Kazinga Channel, so we decided to watch near some of these at dusk. It would obviously be rather a hit or miss choice, but it was worth trying and if we saw no carnivores it would not be without its interest.

We found a hole which looked fairly promising on the rather steep slope of the channel near the euphorbias where the marabous roosted. We thought the birds would add interest to the vigil. Both species of euphorbia were there, but it was obvious from the masses of excreta that it was *Euphorbia dawei* which was the favourite for roosting. This species had a main stem with more or less horizontal branches, compared with the commoner *Euphorbia candelabrum* which had no main trunk, the many branches turning up almost vertically to form a thick top. Many of the first species had been badly damaged by the birds, and a few had already been killed.

We arrived well before dusk to get into a good position without disturbance. The evening was clear, and already a few marabous had taken up their positions on the pinnacles of some of the trees. A few hippos were snorting and grunting in the channel below. Looking up into the sky we saw a large flock of marabous. They came planing in from the west without a single wing beat, like a squadron of aircraft keeping perfect formation. As they neared the line of roosting trees they peeled off to their respective targets, let down their long, spindly legs and landed gracefully. It was a magnificent exhibition of precision flying. There was some squabbling over the best positions, and noisy bill clapping, before they finally settled down for the night.

We had no luck at that hole. No wart-hogs returned, no carnivores emerged! Choosing the right holes when there were so many possibilities was clearly going to be difficult. We needed a lot of luck! We tried again on other occasions, but, although it was always an interesting experience, as far as the carnivores were concerned our luck was out.

Our night watching had shown us that one of the best areas for genets, civets and mongooses was around Hippo Pool. We thought it would be worth getting there before dusk and seeing if anything turned up. If we kept quite still with the engine off we might see far more than by cruising about and looking for eye reflections.

Selection of a suitable site was not easy as there were large numbers of hippos in the pool. How would they treat us if we were in their path when they emerged? There was only one way to find out! The best plan seemed to be to back on to some dense bushes; according to theory they should pass on either side of us if they came near.

When we arrived there were already three hyaenas prowling around the pool and about fifteen elephants could be seen on the far side; several young calves were among them. Near the south-west corner was a herd of about seventy buffalo. The hippos were still in the water, noisy and restless.

We backed into one of the clumps of bushes as planned and turned off the engine. In front we had an uninterrupted view of the pool. There was plenty to watch as the daylight faded. Two garganey teal took flight from the water, winging their way low over the bushes and away. Groups of Egyptian geese clustered in the shallows.

It was almost dark when the first hippo made its lumbering way out of the water. It was followed by several others. Slowly they made their way in single file towards the north-west. We could see that the hippos in the water were grouped together in parties of four or five; each seemed to have its territorial part of the pool and presumably would leave it at the same point. It would be interesting to see. The glow in the sky gave us just enough light to see others emerging from various parts of the water and a huge bull, snorting and wheezing, came out opposite the place where we were parked. It looked as if we were on its territory. It was in no hurry to move and others piled up behind it, impatient to be away.

We could still just make out some of the other hippos following the trails which radiated in all directions from the pool. Then the bull in front of us took a few steps forward and stopped. It had got beyond the lighter background of the water and we could only guess where it was. Which way would it go? We used no headlights so as not to scare it, but kept the spotlight in readiness if we needed it.

We calculated that the bull and his party would pass us a few yards to our right in order to avoid the bushes. We could now see nothing at all, but we could hear their breathing and an occasional snort. How near were they? I put on a small torch and slowly raised it. There was the bull, all two tons of it, standing stock still about ten yards from us. I kept the torch off its eyes and it came forward another few yards. I suddenly remembered the story I had been told of a hippo crunching up the bonnet of a car by the simple process of biting it. It was annoying to think of it at that moment! Should I put the lights on? Should I start the engine just in case?

It came a little nearer, then swung away passing within a few yards of us. Of course it was only common sense that it would behave like that! What was interesting about a Land-Rover to a hippo hungry for good grazing? And yet? Faith in animal behaviour can be misplaced and it certainly looked an enormous monster in the light of that small torch.

We felt better about hippos after that. Others passed us along the same trail, remarkably silent for their huge bulk, but they took no notice of us. They took some time to leave the area, which was a little surprising, as all the grass around had been completely cropped, but their reluctance to leave may have had some territorial significance.

We put on the spotlight at intervals hoping to see some carnivores. Hyaenas were still about and the elephants had made their way to our side of the pool. Later we saw both genet and civet, but we learnt little new of their behaviour as they quickly went off into an area where we couldn't follow.

There was a fish factory at Kabatoro, a rather derelict cluster of Asian-type buildings not far from the main gate of the Park. Large numbers of marabous collected near the factory every day to feed on the fish remains after they had been filleted. We decided to call on the manager, as the place where the offal was dumped might attract civets or mongooses. It might be worth watching. He told us that hyaenas regularly came along to see what there was to eat, but the marabous did not leave much for them. This seemed more than likely, as while we talked rather more than a hundred of these great birds were standing in ranks waiting patiently for the fish remains to be thrown out. He told us that each bird would dispose of at least ten fish skeletons!

He invited us to come back that evening and said he would not throw out the fish remains until we came. It was nearly dark when we returned. A great pile of fish remnants was dumped on the grass not far from the factory and we parked so that our headlights conveniently lit up the area.

We became less hopeful as time went on. We had not reckoned on the factory continuing its activities after dark. Lights blazed, people were talking and cars and trucks came and went. To expect any animals to turn up under these circumstances was certainly asking a lot. Yet within a few minutes we saw the first hyaena come into view, make its way cautiously between the bushes and grab some fish. Two others joined it, and although very wary at first, soon brazenly took what they wanted without bothering at all. We waited for some time, but saw nothing else. It was disappointing.

Apparently it was quite usual for the factory to work well into the night, so with all that noise and light, we felt it was unlikely that we should find it a useful way of seeing the middle-sized carnivores apart from hyaenas.

A method used by hunters for catching some of these smaller carnivores was to trail smelly meat behind the car at dusk and retrace the route later on to see if any had followed the scent trail. We decided to try it.

A visit to William, at the canteen, produced a promise of a large fish. The next day it arrived; an enormous lung fish! It seemed too good for the purpose, but we couldn't be choosers, so we kept it in a polythene bag for thirty-six hours to get high. Then, after dark, we set off hopefully, smelling like a fish manure factory! The lung fish had been divided into two and was tied up ready to attach to the vehicle when we got to a likely place. Two hyaenas met us on their way to visit the dustbins of Mweya; they must have wondered what we had got in the back! Not far on we met a solitary, maned lion on the prowl. It was travelling purposefully as if it had in mind something more acceptable than smelly fish.

A few miles from Mweya, the fish was tied on to the back and bumped behind us as we cruised slowly along. After about five miles of this we turned round and retraced our path. Several hyaenas were seen on the track sniffing the ground as they went; there was little doubt from their behaviour that they were following the trail. Nearer Hippo Pool we saw a fine civet which also appeared to have picked up the scent. We were able to watch it for some time and slowly follow it about without frightening it. It was a very dark specimen, with the black spots covering far more of the surface area than the lighter areas between.

The method seemed promising, so we went over the trail again with the fish still dangling behind. Retracing our route for the last time we seemed to find everything on the track, but quite obviously this had nothing to do with our scent trail! A hippo was particularly obstinate; it just would not get out of the way. It dithered about, going this way and that, but would keep returning to the road. We waited patiently for it to make up its mind which way to go, but clearly it hadn't got a mind to make up. Time was going on and we wanted to follow our trail with as much obstinacy as the hippo. Eventually it went a few yards to the side and appeared to be going off. I decided to help it make its mind up and pass it quickly, but just as I got about level it turned back into the track once more. I braked with a skid on the dusty surface, stopping a yard from the hippo. Very frightened, it reared off in a cloud of dust and then came straight towards us. I reversed remarkably quickly and was quite relieved when it pounded off into the darkness and we were able to get by.

That wasn't the end, because half a mile farther on we came on a cow elephant with two calves of different ages right on the track. We had already met these elephants twice before that night when trailing the fish and grudgingly they had made way for us. This was the last straw for the elephants; we could wait!

We stopped; we advanced; we retreated; we revved the engine. They would not budge! They went on eating from the verge with maddening deliberation. As far as they were concerned we did not exist. The obvious thing was to make a detour over the rough, but a ditch and bank by the side of the track didn't make this easy in the darkness. However, we had little option. We got across and cautiously made a detour between the dense bushes. When level with the elephants on the track we rounded a bush and came face to face with another elephant we hadn't reckoned with. Fortunately it was as surprised as we were and to our relief gave us a free passage.

We saw more hyaenas on the way home and another civet, so altogether it had been a useful trip. Another time we tried high buffalo meat instead of fish, but it appeared to be no improvement on ripe lung fish.

We concluded that the technique was a help for sighting hyaenas and civets especially, but it would get us little farther in our search for where they lived.

Our son Andrew joined us for six weeks at the end of January. We were very glad to have his help with the investigations, so on every suitable night we continued our searching.

Getting back from one of our night expeditions more than ready for bed, we switched on the light and Andrew saw the tail of a snake disappear behind the bookcase. We moved it slightly and a black head poked out from underneath. We didn't know the species of snakes very well; it could have been a cobra or one of the harmless species which fed on mice and rats in the thatch. We wished we knew. Anyway we couldn't leave it there, so we took a few precautions. We put on glasses in case it was a spitting cobra, cleared away surplus furniture from that part of the room and moved the bookcase. The snake was in the corner – very dark, with no obvious markings, four to five feet long and a little more than an inch in diameter. I looked for the inflated hood when it reared up, to show it was a cobra, but its neck appeared quite normal.

The next thing was to catch it! A fairly large sheet of plywood held vertically seemed to be a reasonable way of confining the snake to the corner. The plan was to get it into a long-handled butterfly net with the help of a stick. It was not very co-operative as its one object was to escape. It did not appear to be very aggressive, but at one point Betty heard a hiss and felt something hit her leg which could have been venom. She went and washed it off!

Somehow it got away from the corner into the big fire-place and it looked as if it might escape up the great chimney, but fortunately we cornered it and somehow got it into the net.

The next thing was to get it from the net into something it could be kept in safely. The only receptacle to hand was a large aluminium cooking pot. The net was carefully inverted and the piece of plywood slid over the top. It was with some relief that we inverted a small table on top to prevent it forcing up the ply. By this time we were fairly certain it was a cobra, but we were still not quite sure as it had shown no sign of inflating a hood.

The next morning we asked for expert help over the identification. We slid a piece of glass in place of the ply to get a good view of it and the snake immediately identified itself most obligingly by rearing up, inflating its hood and spitting venom repeatedly at the glass! It was strange that it hadn't done this the previous night, but presumably it had recently fed and was more intent on escape. Perhaps it was as well!

Spitting cobras are said to be able to eject venom eight feet or more. We didn't put this to the test, but the twin jets which shot from the hollow fangs certainly hit the glass with some force. When a cobra spits it vigorously contracts the muscles round the poison sacs and forces the venom out through its short fangs under considerable pressure.

The next problem was what to do with it? We had no lack of

advice! But this was a National Park with special regulations about killing animals! We decided to release it in a part of the Park where it could do no harm.

It made a somewhat unusual travelling companion in the back of the Land-Rover, but we took precautions and it arrived safely at a place well away from any track. It was released with some care, and it moved away rapidly through the short grass and disappeared into a dense bush, giving us little chance to photograph it.

Having explored the immediate neighbourhood of Mweya very thoroughly over a number of weeks and still found no den where any of the medium-sized carnivores were living, we decided to investigate the Nyamugasani and Kayanja region of the Park beyond Katwe. We had seen this part previously from the air and it looked most attractive, but it had the disadvantage of being rather far from Mweya for repeated visits.

Our first trip was by day and mainly exploratory. We had to leave the Park by the main gate and follow the road past Kabatoro to Katwe, the large fishing village we were able to see from Mweya on the far shore of Lake Edward. On closer inspection it turned out to be a dusty, sprawling, squalid assemblage of huts and dukas with little to commend it. A few miles farther you could enter the Park again and follow a track which led to the Ranger Post at Nyamugasani.

The view from this Ranger Post was magnificent. You looked across the Nyamugasani River as it flowed in a series of snake-like contortions towards Lake Edward. On either side of the river there was dense forest which looked very exciting, but difficult to penetrate. A brilliant, red flame tree stood out conspicuously among the varied greens of the close-packed trees. There were large stretches of papyrus swamp where a few elephants were feeding up to their bellies in water.

Farther to the right was Pelican Point, stretching farther into Lake Edward. It was a famous place for birds. The country at the back of Pelican Point was drier and grassy and seemed ideal for seeing the middle-sized carnivores as the grass was shorter than near Mweya. There were many more termite mounds and numerous wart-hog holes, so there were plenty of potential dens for these animals.

The region was a good one for kob, an antelope which was not plentiful in the immediate vicinity of Mweya. As we approached, several quite large herds were making their way towards the lake. Returning later in the day we saw them again; they had combined to form a mas-

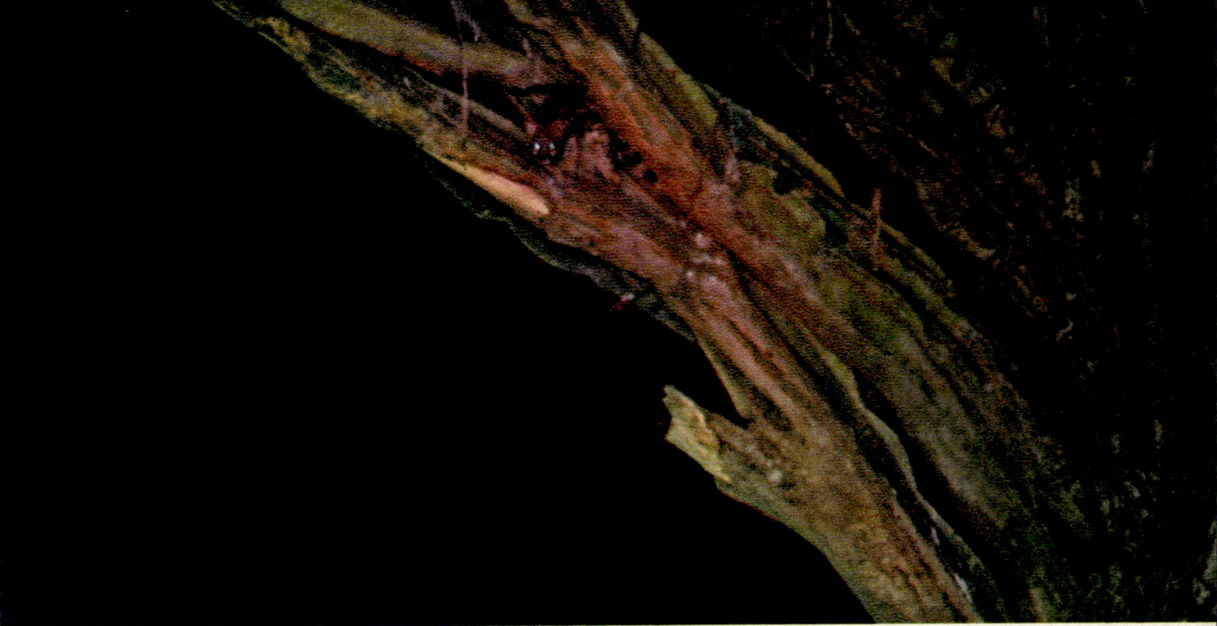

8. Genet in a euphorbia tree (by flashlight)

9. Spotted hyaena yawning

10. Lake fish; two tilapia and a barbel

11. Lungfish

12. White-necked cormorants

13. Marabou stork

14. Yellow-billed stork

15. Saddle-billed storks

sive assembly of several hundred animals which swept past us as we watched them. They looked magnificent in the sunshine with their bright, reddish-brown coats.

Our main objective that day was the Kayanja region a few miles past the Nyamugasani Ranger Post. Here the trees and bushes became more dense and the termite mounds more frequent. In one of these we found signs of a lot of digging and there were more excavations over a wide area surrounding the mound. These looked different from the more usual rootings and diggings of wart-hogs, so we inspected them more closely. Eventually we found the three-toed prints of the aardvark, or ant bear. One freshly-made hole of large diameter which led to the heart of the termite mound had a pile of freshly moved earth outside and you could see the narrow groove in it which had been made by the tail of the aardvark as it had entered or left.

Termite mounds were used for many purposes by the local fauna. Besides being used as refuges for the aardvark and wart-hog, they provided rubbing posts for the bigger animals. Those near the lake were often worn smooth by hippos rubbing against them. More isolated mounds in grassy areas were used by kob as viewpoints and appeared to be important to the older males as territorial markers. The mounds were also used as feeding places: a half-eaten fish we found on the top of one of them was the remains of a fish eagle's meal that morning.

Other animals habitually used termite mounds when defaecating, as rabbits use ant hills in Britain. We found the scats of one of the solitary species of mongoose on several occasions, but we were not sufficiently expert to know whether they belonged to the black-tipped or the great grey.

As we continued our explorations a large pack of banded mongoose ran across into the bushes and we were able to examine the muddy ground for tracks after they had gone, to make certain what they really looked like. It was surprising how little showed when they travelled at speed over the ground, but the pin-hole marks of the sharp claws could be seen clearly. As we gained experience in tracking we found these tiny marks were quite characteristic of the species and a sure way of recognizing that a pack had travelled that way.

A new bird to us at Kayanja was the black-chested harrier eagle. The head was comparatively large compared with most eagles and was almost owl-like in appearance. The chest was black and the belly pure white with no spots on it. It flew from one vantage point to another as we approached it.

We visited this area of the Park on a number of occasions by day and got to know it quite well, and although rather far from Mweya we thought we should also explore it by night, as it certainly looked a good place for the carnivores.

The plan was to get there early and watch quietly near the hole where we had seen signs of aardvark and then patrol the region after dark to look for any carnivores.

In the morning we had looked out on Lake Edward from Mweya and seen what appeared to be three columns of smoke rising from the water quite far out. This turned out to be a great hatch of lake flies. It was not until we had parked in a strategic place that evening, down wind from the aardvark hole, that we remembered them, because by that time the wind currents had brought them to the shore and they were all round us in their billions. Then we saw the martins. At first there were just a few, then the numbers increased and in a few minutes they were everywhere. There were thousands and thousands of martins hawking the flies in every direction. How they managed to avoid collision seemed a miracle as they gave a fantastic exhibition of aerobatics in front of us. Wherever you looked, the sky was full of martins.

All the time the light was gradually going and we noticed a subtle change in their behaviour. Instead of flying in an apparently random manner as they snapped up the lake flies, we noticed they were now mainly going in one direction and soon they were definitely heading for the west, presumably to their roosting places before it got too dark. The numbers soon thinned out as they sped westwards and became reduced to isolated groups, 'hedge-hopping' like starlings returning at dusk to their roosts in Britain. It was an amazing sight to have witnessed.

We had parked about fifty feet from the aardvark den, but as yet there was no sign of the animal itself. A bushbuck came out of one of the dense clumps of bushes and started to browse. It must have been near us all the time, but we had not noticed it previously. A second soon joined it and they moved off together towards another clump of bushes to browse.

There was a fine sunset over the lake and the Congo Mountains stood out clearly in the distance. Nine greater egrets flew past with the glow catching the white of their wings as they flew, their long black legs trailing behind them. A nightjar settled on the ground quite silently just four yards away; another settled farther on and they both started to churr loudly to herald the night. We made a tape recording of their strangely monotonous call. The crickets, too, were very noisy, keeping up an incessant background of stridulation. Mosquitoes were now getting into the Land-Rover and were rather too persistent in their attentions. We wished that aardvark would appear!

It was now very dark and we strained our eyes through binoculars for any sign of movement, but nothing showed. Later on we used a torch at intervals, but the same empty hole stared back at us. It was like badger watching all over again – just one of those nights when nothing happens! We waited on, but the odds were now heavily against it appearing, so we decided to press on farther and see what eyes the spotlight would pick up. We cautiously followed what track there was for several miles. Bats would occasionally come into the beam as they took their toll of the lake flies left by the martins; occasionally a hippo would cross the track on its way to graze. We had our first bit of luck when we saw a pair of brilliant eyes shine back at us from the base of a large euphorbia. We approached it very slowly and a fine genet came into proper view, sitting upright like a cat, watching us. As we were on a slope, I switched off the engine and quietly slid towards it in neutral, stopping about ten yards from it.

Using the spotlight with a red filter we were able to watch it for a long time without disturbing it. It started to climb the euphorbia like a squirrel, keeping to the far side of the trunk and poking its head round every now and then to look at us. It held its long ringed tail quite straight and kept its body close to the tree as it climbed. Edging its way along one of the branches, it stopped and started to wash itself, cleaning its face with one paw like a cat.

After we had watched it for some time I decided to try for a photo; but we were thirty feet away, and starting the engine again to get nearer would probably have frightened it. I did the best I could with a small telephoto and not unexpectedly the genet disappeared at speed when the flash went off. We saw another genet farther on, but it quietly vanished into a bush.

We were now returning towards the Nyamugasani Ranger Post and the more open country behind. If there were carnivores about we ought to be able to see them in the shorter grass. We had not long to wait. A pair of eyes, rather low down and very bright, showed up far over to our left. We turned off the track to get a better view and found it was a civet. Perhaps it was on its way to look for scraps near the Ranger Post. We followed it for a time, but it was very wary and catching sight of other eyes we switched our attention to their owner; it was a white-tailed mongoose. It was not unduly disturbed by our attentions, but ambled off in the direction of Pelican Point.

It was only a matter of minutes afterwards that we saw another genet, the third that night. This one appeared to be a younger animal, but it disappeared by a termite mound and although we looked carefully we could not see any sign of a den. It was puzzling.

We had already had a long day so we decided to make our way home, but before we left that part of the Park we saw one more carnivore: this time it was a serval. As in all our encounters with servals, the grass was long here. It showed the usual unconcern after watching us carefully for a few moments and then continued its slow precise movements as it continued its hunting.

It was very late when we got back to Mweya. The gate across the road was padlocked and the guards fast asleep. It was a long time before they heard us and appeared at the gate armed with a rifle in case of trouble. Nobody was very pleased!

Other night visits to that part of the Park confirmed that it was a good area for most of the carnivore species. One of these visits had its amusing side, if that is the right way of describing it.

We intended to get there early, but soon after we set out we came across a pride of lions making their way towards us as if out for an evening stroll. They passed on both sides of the car with hardly a look in our direction – fifteen of them.

When we got to the Nyamugasani area dusk was falling and we made a short cut across rough country behind the Ranger Post to save time. It didn't turn out like that, because half way across we got a flat tyre. This should have been no problem; I jacked it up and went to the tool chest for the wheel brace, only to find it wasn't there! Tool kits were regularly inspected in NUTAE vehicles for obvious reasons, but somebody had slipped up. No other tool made any impression on the wheel nuts! It was now nearly dark, there was game about and the Ranger Post was about 600 yards away and could be seen on the skyline. Luckily the ground was grassy, reasonably flat and not too hard, so we decided, in spite of possible damage to the tyre, to go carefully on towards the Ranger Post and get help. We got there without further mishap.

Several families were living there and everybody was very helpful, but the two Rangers had not yet returned. While a crowd of children watched proceedings and the women finished cooking the supper, two of the men tried their hand at the wheel. They had no wheel brace of course and the adjustable spanner we had used was no more effective in their hands. Those nuts would not budge! The Rangers returned soon afterwards. They had just walked back from the Kayanja Post five miles away and were tired after the day's work. They too tried the wheel, but to no avail.

The Rangers proposed that they should accompany us and we would walk to Katwe, nearly five miles away, and possibly get a car to take us to Mweya. We gratefully accepted their offer and after a quick bite of supper we started off.

It was a lovely night and the walk could be quite exciting. We very much wanted to see how the Rangers would react to buffalo or elephant if we came across them. One had a rifle and the other a spear, but neither would be used except in an emergency. We made good progress and although we kept peering into the darkness we saw no game of any size – it was quite disappointing!

Eventually we reached the main Katwe road and crossed the river. Over the marshy region beside it the fireflies gave a fine display, tracing their paths in streaks of light in many directions. It was astonishing how they kept switching on and off!

The Rangers were in very good humour. One of them could speak English quite well, and the hour and a half went by quite quickly before we reached the village. The Rangers spotted a Land-Rover outside one of the bars and to our relief it belonged to the Park authorities. After drinks, the driver agreed to take us all back to the Post and change the wheel for us. We could then make our way back in our own vehicle. It would not take long!

We sped back once more along the track we knew so well, bumping along regardless. The driver excusably must have thought what fools we had been to come out without all the tools. On arrival he unlocked his own tool box and there was a moment of silence – his wheel brace was missing too! It was almost funny, but not quite! But he was not to be beaten and with the help of a hammer and steel bit he got the nuts off, but it took forty-five minutes to do the job!

After that all was plain sailing. The nuts of the spare wheel were tightened as best we could and we drove back slowly in case the wheel should come off. We got back quite tired, having been up since five o'clock that morning doing a dawn watch in another part of the Park. No elephant woke us up that night!

So far we had gathered considerable experience of the general ecology of the Park and we felt we knew the commoner animals quite well and were beginning to be familiar with some of the commoner carnivores; but still we were no further forward over finding their dens.

By now I was fairly convinced that radio-telemetry was going to be the only way of finding them, apart from a lot of luck. This would mean live trapping the animal first, attaching a minute radio transmitter to it by means of a collar or harness and letting it go again. It could then be followed by picking up the signals, using a recorder and head-phones. In this way you could find out where it was living in the daytime and at night it could be followed and with good fortune watched for prolonged periods.

It was, of course, a highly specialized technique, as the correct method of attachment of the transistor had to be found experimentally for each species; animals being notoriously good at slipping out of collars unless they are exactly the right size.

The method had been used successfully on a number of animals in Europe and America and I had hoped to use it during this trip. We were disappointed when the equipment did not arrive and so were unable to try it out ourselves. However, as it turned out, it was probably not a bad thing as our time was strictly limited and we could probably not have done much with it in the time available.

But what could we try next? Fortunately our day work on the banded mongoose was becoming much more promising and from the middle of February we decided to concentrate our attention on them, a campaign that is described in full in Chapter Six.

CHAPTER THREE

The Attraction of Water

The presence of Lakes Edward and George, with the Kazinga Channel connecting them has had a tremendous effect on the whole fauna of the Queen Elizabeth National Park. Many of the complex food chains have their origins in the prolific phytoplankton in these lakes. Here the vital process of photosynthesis occurs at a high rate in the warm water and the fauna exploits this to the full by feeding on these microscopic algae either directly or indirectly.

There are plentiful supplies of nutrients in these lakes. Hippos are constantly depositing great quantities of dung in the water to add to the other raw materials for bacterial decomposition, and plant growth is rapid in consequence.

Fish grow fast under these conditions and their population density is very high in these lakes. It is the fish population that forms a key industry which is not only exploited by man, but also by a host of other animals in the Park, including many of the larger birds.

The main food fish for the human population is tilapia. These have an average weight of just over a pound and are caught by the African fishermen in great numbers. Up to three million fish a year have been captured in Lake George alone, but numbers are now said to be declining.

We watched the fishermen on the Kazinga Channel setting their nets in a semi-circle and then thrashing the water with a long stick to drive the fish into the net.

Most of the fish were taken to the fish factories where they were filleted and frozen; others were split and sun-dried or smoked.

Although most of the fishing is centred on Lakes Edward and George, some of the smaller lakes in the Park have their quota of fishing canoes, and on one occasion we visited Nyamusingire Lake which is surrounded by dense forest.

We followed a track which was much overgrown. The grass on it was higher than the bonnet of the Volkswagen, but we ploughed on hopefully for about twelve miles, avoiding termite mounds and the wetter areas. Eventually we arrived at the Ranger Post at Mukolobezi at the base of the escarpment. From there we took a rather better track to the Ranger Post on the edge of the Nyamusingire Lake. On our way we met many people carrying fish on long poles: the only method of transporting them from the lake.

At the Post the Ranger showed us the way the fish were treated. Down by the lake they were being gutted and washed, and a large number of green and black swallow tail butterflies was drinking at the water's edge where fish juices from the washing had collected. Back in the clearing, fish were being salted and sun-dried. Only two canoes were allowed to fish on this rather small lake to conserve the numbers, tilapia being the main fish taken.

When they spawn, tilapia choose the margins of the lake where there is much vegetation; here they are safe from the fishermen. They look after their eggs by incubating them in their mouths, and later protect the fry (after they have hatched) in the same way.

Another most interesting fish we came across was the lung fish. We were visiting Pelican Point beyond Katwe when we saw some Africans wading in a shallow area covered in Nile cabbage and other vegetation. The men slowly worked their way along, prodding just in front of them with long spears. The fish lie in the mud and if speared thrash about violently. When one was caught it was tied to a strong cord and dragged laboriously behind the fisherman as he continued his methodical spearing.

He showed us two that he had dumped on land and tied to a tree in case they got away! They were large fish, twenty pounds at least, but we were told they sometimes reached 100 lbs.

Lung fish are most curious fish to look at with their thread-like pectoral and pelvic fins which they use like limbs for propelling themselves along the surface of the mud.

Having lungs as well as gills, they are able to breathe air if the shallow waters should dry up. If this happens they burrow into the mud and secrete a lot of slime which binds the mud into a cement-like cocoon on drying. An opening is left which connects with the outside by a vertical shaft through which the encysted fish can breathe. When the rains return the mud softens and they can swim away. Lung fish have been known to exist in their mud cocoons for as long as four years, feeding internally on their tissues. The emaciated fish which eventually emerge are mere shadows of their original selves having lost so much weight, but they soon feed up and regenerate their lost tissues.

Man is not the only species to exploit the fish population and on many occasions we watched some of the larger birds which competed very successfully with the fishermen.

Two species of pelican were commonly seen, the white and pink-backed. They fished with remarkable precision. You would see a group of them near the edge of the lake forming an arc and then, as if by word of command, all would plunge their beaks into the water simultaneously. In this way the fish are driven into a smaller compass and many are caught. They keep the fish in the pouch just long enough for the water to drain out before swallowing it. The pouch is said to be large enough to hold almost three gallons of water.

The herons fished in a very different way. The goliath, biggest of them all with a height of over four feet, characteristically stood in the shallows like a statue waiting for prey to approach. Great white egrets stalked slowly forward, necks bent and bills pointed downwards ready to strike at the first movement. Purple herons were rare, but we saw one near Pelican Point hunting for food in and out of the taller marsh vegetation, its colour blending beautifully in this type of habitat. We saw squacco herons there too, shorter and more thickset, with buff plumage and white wings which showed up prominently when they flew.

Not all the herons were fish eaters by any means, some were certainly hunting for frogs and a few were mainly insectivorous. When elephant or buffalo came near the water the cattle egrets were usually in attendance. Some were settled on their backs, others were on the mud weaving their way between the legs of the animals. It was interesting to see how they exploited the presence of the larger animals, pecking at the insects which were disturbed by their movements.

Large numbers of cormorants were regularly seen on their favourite beaches beside the Kazinga Channel. The commonest were the white-necked and long-tailed. They usually fed far out on the lake, returning to their beaches to rest communally. They also congregated on the euphorbia trees which bordered the lake and channel. The very rare Uganda cormorant was also seen alongside the white-necked. They are only known from the two main lakes of Queen Elizabeth Park and the Kazinga Channel and appear to be nearly related to the European cormorant, but how they got there is a mystery. They differ from the white-necked by having far less white; instead of the white throat and chest of the former, this bird appears black all over except for a white head and white thigh patches. The eye colour is also different, green in the Uganda and red in the white-necked. The long-tailed is a much smaller bird.

Other birds which exploited the fish population were the kingfishers. It was impossible not to be captivated by these lovely birds. The commonest was the pied. One would fly out from a perch on the bank of the channel, hover above the water, body held still, but with head constantly moving as it scanned the water for fish before making a dive. Many times they would think better of it before reaching the water, and few of the actual dives produced a fish, but as they kept it up most of the day they presumably caught plenty for their needs.

The smallest and most brilliant kingfisher was the malachite – a gem of a bird with upper parts brilliant ultramarine and underparts rufous. It differs from the rather similar pygmy by its white cheeks and the prominent crest of feathers on its head. The pygmy was the less common of the two.

There are several islands in Lake Edward, two of which we visited. The larger, called Izinga, had a shore that was sloping only slightly and it was possible for hippo to get on to it and graze. Near Izinga was a smaller island with much steeper sides which hippo were unable to climb. The consequent difference in vegetation was remarkable, the smaller island being covered with dense vegetation including a lot of trees, whereas the larger had mainly thorny scrub which had defied the efforts of the hippos.

I was intrigued to find hyaena droppings on the island, as it was only a small one and rather more than a mile from the mainland. How they had got there was a mystery.

We got good views of a greater kestrel which appeared to be nesting in one of the tallest trees. It was a fine-looking bird with a bluish grey tail boldly barred with black.

From Izinga we went to the rather larger island of Kabazimu. On landing, a five foot monitor lizard ran up the bank into a bush at great speed. These large lizards were commonly seen near the channel and round the margins of the lakes. The younger ones are black, speckled with yellow, but as they get older they tend to become a duller greyish brown. Their colour often blended very well with the surroundings. In the Murchison Falls National Park they are important predators of crocodile eggs, but in Queen Elizabeth Park they appear to live more on fish. We saw one eating a tilapia, and on another occasion had the good fortune to see a big monitor bring an immense catfish out of the Channel. The fish was very long and the monitor had it by the neck and was straddling it as it dragged the fish up the bank.

There were euphorbia trees on Kabazimu and at least four of them contained goliath heron nests with eggs. The birds were loath to leave them when we approached and soon returned when we had passed by.

In the recent past, victims from tribal wars had been taken from the mainland and left on this island by the local chief. It was said that old people, too, had met with a similar fate. The vultures did the rest. We found no human skeletons on this occasion!

A solitary elephant was grazing on the island. The surrounding water was probably shallow enough for it to have waded across from the mainland, trunk raised, without resorting to swimming. Elephants will go to considerable lengths to find food when the ground is parched and this one had possibly scented the vegetation from afar and braved the crossing to reach it. An adult is said to need between three and four hundred pounds of vegetation a day to keep it going, so an island with lush grazing could be a great attraction during the dry season.

Some of the largest water birds were the storks. Not all are fish eaters but the majority of species were seen by water. The marabous were by far the most grotesque. They were true scavengers, eating anything that came their way. We watched one solemnly attempting to swallow a twelve-inch piece of iron tubing; it tried for some time and very nearly succeeded. It is difficult to imagine what would have happened if it had!

One evening we were watching the marabous coming back to their roost and landing on the euphorbias with their usual precision when suddenly a tremendous wind sprang up and the birds had great difficulty in keeping their perches. Many were forced to take to the air again but the wind kept blowing them off course making landing very difficult. They seemed to take delight in dislodging others which had made good landings, flying up into the air together flapping their wings, snapping their bills and uttering warning cries as they fought for roosting places. When a marabou tried to land where a group of pelicans was roosting, the defenders all pointed their sharp bills upwards and the marabou wisely went elsewhere.

A much more handsome bird than the marabou is the yellow-billed stork. We came across a large group of these in a small pool on Lake George flats. Usually we saw them in ones or twos, but here there were at least ten of them, adults and juveniles, along with a few sacred ibis. When close we could see every detail of their magnificent plumage. The back which appeared so white from a distance was in fact suffused with pale pink and the brilliant yellow bill projecting from the red head was in striking contrast. When they took off they circled majestically overhead showing the contrasting black tops to the white wings.

The most spectacular storks of all were the saddle-billed. We saw them first on the marsh beyond Hippo Pool, pacing slowly across the wet ground, looking for frogs in the mud. Over four feet tall, they looked the true aristocrats of the bird world. The black bill is coloured pillar-box red at both ends, and the so-called saddle is a golden yellow structure attached on top of the red base. We never saw many at a time, but always they gave an air of real distinction to any group of birds they were with.

The marsh attracted a great variety of birds; you never knew what would turn up. One morning there were five woolly-necked storks there, along with a pair of saddle-billed. The former were new to us, but quite unmistakable with their dark bodies, curiously woolly looking necks and dark bills. They were hunting most successfully for bull frogs which were buried in the wet mud. On the same occasion a fine African marsh harrier was quartering the area probably intent on the same prey: the bars on the wing tips and tail were conspicuous when it flew near with typical harrier flight.

It was here too that we saw fan-tailed widow birds – black birds with patches of rusty orange at the base of the wings. When they flew, more of this colour showed across the back. They were clinging to the reeds in the manner of reed buntings in Britain.

We found that some of these inland sources of water were quite as interesting as the Kazinga Channel and the margins of the lakes. Hippo Pool itself was always worth scanning and its population of birds was constantly changing. Egyptian geese were permanent residents and in January there were several broods of tiny goslings. It was a study in contrast to see a bull buffalo wading through the shallow water and a mother with her brood of perhaps nine goslings nimbly avoiding this massive intrusion into her territory. There were usually plenty of waders to watch, the daintiest being the black-winged stilts, their incredibly long, thin, pink legs supporting their black and white bodies and long straight bills high above the water. Spur-wing plover always looked very prim and well turned out when standing quietly at the water's edge, while the minute Kittlitz's sand plover made rapid runs on tiny legs, pausing briefly to snatch at some insect. When still, they blended wonderfully with their background.

Many waders were usually present as this was the European winter season and many had migrated. There were little stints, several species of sandpipers, greenshanks and spotted redshanks. The only species of duck was the garganey teal which was always there in good numbers.

On the far side you usually saw a hammerkop. These strange thick-set brown birds with heavy crests would stand contemplatively on the mud near the water's edge or on the back of a hippo. One wondered what they were thinking about! Their nests, which we found in several parts of the Park in large acacia trees, were enormous structures made of a big erection of sticks, mud and grass. They looked quite solid but there was an opening on one side which led into the central chamber where the eggs were laid.

Another bird of rather unusual appearance was the water dikkop, a species of stone curlew with characteristic thick knees. A pair was often to be seen on the mud near the water's edge.

But Hippo Pool without the hippos would be a sad sight. Their sheer ugliness made them most attractive. During the day they appeared to be scattered all over the pool, but in fact their distribution was by no means random as each school kept more or less to its own territory. They stood nearly submerged to keep themselves cool. If completely exposed too long to the fierce sun they are said to suffer from sunburn!

Every now and then there would be some movement and a younger male might come closer than it should to the dominant bull. This always led to vigorous display. The dominant bull would hold its head upright and open its mouth to its fullest extent, displaying the big tusks to its rival. This might be quite enough to cause the other to turn round and make off, but sometimes the display would be returned and the two huge animals would face each other with their mouths open. On one occasion when this happened the owner of the territory lowered its head slightly so that its lower jaw was well under water, then it closed its mouth vigorously. This caused a wave of water to enter the other's mouth with great force. This too seemed to have no effect and both bulls started to roar at each other. As part of the display they took it in turns to defaecate, lashing the dung with their tails and spreading it over a wide area. The water was whipped into foam when the territorial bull chased its rival away from his school of cows and calves.

When one bull goes for another in earnest it does not actually bite it, but hits the other with its open jaws. In this way the tusks make contact with the flesh of the other and it gives an upward thrust. We saw several with ugly gashes on their sides resulting from fights of this kind.

Hippos, when nearly submerged, make good landing grounds for waders, which run over their bodies as if they were rocks. On one very hot day we saw strange objects on the backs of some of the hippos which we could not recognize. Through the binoculars we saw that they were quite large tortoises which had left the water and were basking on these convenient platforms. They were probably hinged tortoises, so called because the under side of the carapace is flexible in one place. They were not uncommon in the pool, but were seldom seen until the water began to dry up in the hot weather.

Monitor lizards often hunted along the edge of the pool, their black forked tongues darting in and out in the manner of snakes as they felt their way along.

For some of the fauna, water was not just a habitat where food could be obtained, but it served subsidiary purposes. Both elephant and buffalo used to visit Hippo Pool to drink and also to bathe.

The elephants came in family groups, making a leisurely trek towards the water. A cow would usually lead the procession and another would bring up the rear. Sometimes several families would come together and line up at the edge of the water; then the ritual of drinking would begin. They never drank simultaneously and we got the impression that there were always some on the alert while others were drinking.

What an astonishing adaptation the trunk is! A much modified elongated nose, and yet used for drinking, feeding, carrying, and, of course, scenting. When drinking the trunk was held out almost straight and a lot of water sucked up, then it was bent towards the open mouth and the water squirted down the throat. When grazing, the trunk was twisted round the rank tufts of grass, which were pulled up and stuffed into the mouth. It was also capable of carrying out the most delicate operations, picking up the smallest fruits by using the sensitive lips at the end of the trunk. The trunk had a dual role when feeding, because being a nose it selected by scent the particular thing it wished to eat. On one occasion we watched an elephant down by Katunguru Creek carefully going over the moist mud with its trunk and putting small fragments into its mouth; it was probably searching for salts in the ground.

In very hot weather, especially, elephants used to bathe in Hippo Pool. The water was too shallow to do this easily and they would lie on their sides to get as much covered as possible. They seemed to resent being disturbed when bathing. One day we found three on their sides in the water; they were youngish males. We approached to get a photograph, but their response was immediate. They got up hastily, trumpeted in rage and charged in our direction. It was unlikely that they would have pressed their attack, but we didn't put it to the test and took avoiding action.

They also loved to go to wallows, fill their trunks up with liquid mud and squirt it over their backs and behind their ears. This helped to keep them cool. They flapped their great ears for the same purpose, as in this way they increased the surface area of their bodies by about a third. The inner surface of the ear is well supplied with blood vessels and much heat is lost through them.

Buffalo also like the proximity of water and there were always a few old bulls not far from Hippo Pool. They spent a lot of time sitting in the shallows, sometimes plastered all over with mud when the sun was particularly hot. Yellow-billed oxpeckers perched on their backs and searched for ticks and blood-sucking flies; they systematically did the rounds of their clients. They were yellowish birds, the size of a starling, with a yellow beak tipped with red.

It was near Hippo Pool that we came across a new-born elephant. It was standing with its mother in the centre of a rather large clearing more or less surrounded by bushes. Other elephants were spaced out round the perimeter browsing on the bushes. The baby was so small its head only reached up to the beginning of the hairy end of its mother's tail. It could not have been more than three feet high, probably even smaller. The mother was a large animal and it would have been quite impossible for her baby to reach her teats to suckle unless she knelt down.

The baby stood motionless with head bowed, eyes closed and its tiny trunk half supported on the drying mud. The only sign of life was an occasional slight flap of the ears.

The mother kept close to her baby all the time, periodically feeding on some of the coarse grass within reach. Then she gave herself a mud bath, blowing the mud from her trunk under her belly and behind her ears.

We watched from a distance, as all the surrounding elephants appeared to be rather edgy. When there is a very young calf about it is always wise not to go too near, and this was no time to disturb them.

After a few minutes a huge male elephant entered the arena and went up to the cow, smelling her hindquarters with his trunk. He did the same with the baby, scenting it all over most carefully. The other elephants round the perimeter took no notice. To us this seemed clearly to be a recognition ceremony by the father.

Betty was in the open back of the Land-Rover and we were both completely absorbed, watching the drama through binoculars and taking photographs. Suddenly there was an urgent rap on the cab roof and a peremptory 'go'! I couldn't see what was happening behind, but I reacted promptly. The first time the engine wouldn't start, but fortunately it responded the second time and we got away in a cloud of dust. Betty told me later that while we were both watching the family, another large elephant had silently approached from the rear; when she first saw it, it was already near and when we finally got away it was only about ten yards from us and coming steadily on. It was certainly seeing us off the premises! Betty characteristically got a picture of the elephant just as we moved off!

We came across a lot more elephants farther on and several of them made curious snorting sounds through their trunks as we passed. They clearly wanted to be left alone, so we turned our attention elsewhere.

16. Malachite kingfisher on papyrus

17. Lily-trotter walking on floating Nile cabbage

18. Marabou storks and sacred ibis

19. School of hippos in the Kazinga Channel

20. Bull hippo showing aggression

21. Grasshopper showing flash colouration when about to fly
22. A well-camouflaged grasshopper

CHAPTER FOUR

The Larger Carnivores

Lions are not uncommon in Queen Elizabeth Park and being unafraid of people and vehicles they are comparatively easily watched.

There were various prides which hunted over large areas of savannah in different regions; each pride was markedly territorial. The pride we knew best was a large one, over twenty animals. Its composition varied from time to time and it was often split up into two groups, the larger containing fifteen to seventeen animals. In this larger group there were usually three adult maned lions, several lionesses, four or five young animals approaching maturity and some younger cubs.

The family groups had combined to form a large unit which was effective both for hunting and at the same time looking after the younger animals, two vital functions of lion society.

The maned lions were not always with the rest when we came across them, but they usually appeared when there was a kill, to take their share.

Having large territories you never knew where they would be from one day to the next, but we got the impression that they worked a particular area for a few weeks and then left it in favour of another. No doubt the various game herds got used to the presence of lions and became more wary if the lions remained in one spot for long.

Our first sight of the pride was on Christmas Day. There were sixteen on that occasion, mainly resting in the shade of bushes and trees. They had presumably made a kill not far away and were largely satiated after their meal.

A week later we saw them again; this time on a kill. A large bull buffalo had been brought down and the pride was making the most of the meal. Two maned lions had already eaten their fill and were lying in the grass to one side, but the rest were still busily feeding.

We wondered what the succession of events would be, from the time the prey was killed to the point when the last bones were gnawed.

What other animals would play a part? Hyaenas and vultures presumably, but what of the middle-sized carnivores, would they have a share? Strangely enough, there were no jackals in this part of the Park. A large kill like a buffalo would provide a lot of food and the whole sequence would take at least twenty-four hours. It could be exciting to watch during the night, so we decided we would do so at the first good opportunity.

One morning, when looking for tracks near Hippo Pool, we came across a mature male lion resting beside a bush. When it got up, it dragged its hind limb badly. We found out later that it had had an injury several years before when it was a cub; a car had run into it after dark. It had made a good recovery, but it was unable to take much part in hunting and was largely dependent on the rest of the pride for food. We saw this animal on various occasions. The pride always allowed him to feed, but he was seldom there when the kill was made and caught up with the pride later. Although his condition was reasonably good, there were times when food was insufficient and he always looked rather thin.

The lame lion was of course very easily recognizable, and on the occasion when we first watched the pride at night he became the centre of a most exciting drama which brought out an interesting aspect of the social behaviour of lions.

The pride made a kill in the late evening. It was a large bull buffalo which had probably been rejected by the herd. That night as they fed, the pride made a compact circle round the carcass, each with its head within reach of some part of the body. They certainly economized in space as all fifteen lions were able to feed at the same time. The noise of their feeding was punctuated by angry growls and gruff protests if a neighbour poached on another's preserves. Occasionally a more dominant animal would get up and force itself into another part of the circle.

After some hours the majority was filled to capacity, and one by one they retreated a few yards to sleep it off, leaving the kill to the younger animals which had not done so well. It was a weird scene as we watched from the Land-Rover parked a few yards from the kill. Lions were sprawling on the grass in various states of satiation, some were asleep, others were restlessly rolling on their backs from side to side, apparently too full to sleep. The carcass was never completely deserted as they seemed to take it in turns to return and have another half-hearted meal. They saw to it that no hyaenas came near. It was probably in the very early morning that the lame lion arrived. He was already feeding with two or three others when we came on the scene after breakfast.

As the sun rose higher the lions took less interest in the kill. Most of them retired to rest in the bushes nearby, seeking shade from the heat of the sun. Two immature males, a lioness and the lame lion went on eating. Vultures had gathered, some in euphorbia trees and others in huddled groups patiently waiting for their turn. Hyaenas were nowhere to be seen, although there was a den quite near.

Most of the better cuts from the buffalo had long since gone, but the lame lion was working systematically at the flesh between the ribs, rasping it off with the tongue and pulling at the sinews. The head of the kill was largely untouched and the lower parts of the limbs were still intact. We left the scene intending to return before dusk to see the sequel; the lame lion was still feeding, with a lioness for company.

The sun was low when we returned in the evening. A few vultures were circling overhead, but the greater number were standing patiently in a semi-circle, a few were on a large termite mound, others were on trees. Both hooded and white-backed vultures were present.

Ten hyaenas were already on the scene, two were scrapping over the pelvic girdle of the buffalo, others had smaller pieces, but the rest were just waiting around. The main carcass had been dragged from where it had been killed to the side of a bush; all that remained was the rib case, head and the lower limbs with some skin attached. It seemed curious that no hyaenas were actually at the main kill, but on circling the bush in the Land-Rover we found the lame lion crouching nearby; the inference was obvious. No other lions were about, and it appeared that the lame one was guarding the remains with the intention of feeding again later.

We parked about fifteen yards from the carcass in a position where we could use the headlights when it became too dark to see. All was quiet as we watched the hyaenas moving around, taking no notice of us but eyeing the carcass from afar. One went to the termite mound and drove away the vultures that were perched on top. No vulture was feeding. When the light got dim, as if at a signal, the vultures flew off in a body to roost, their patience unrewarded.

Then the chorus began. At first it was tentative and restrained . . . a low call, then an eerie howl, then others joined in and the hyaenas were in full cry. They became much more active and formed a loose circle round the bush where the lion and the carcass were, and incidentally us too. The howling reached a crescendo and then died down again and it was quiet once more. But the hyaenas kept up their movement in a wide circle round the lion. One large animal which was travelling in the opposite direction to the rest, slowed down whenever it came opposite to another one and rubbed its throat against the other's head, which lowered it as it passed. This ritual happened three times before the howling started again.

This time the excitement was greater and the circle began to close in. The lion had its back to the bush as it crouched by the kill lashing its tail furiously. The hyaenas went very near and the lion sprang to its feet and roared repeatedly. Immediately there was silence and the hyaenas retreated out of range and the lion subsided once more. But he was not allowed to relax and the howling started again.

With hyaenas all round us, we were in the centre of a weird and terrifying chorus. The eeriness of the situation gripped you and you imagined how fearful it would be if you were not in the vehicle, and the canvas back of the vehicle suddenly seemed wholly inadequate. The lion was feeling the strain too, surrounded by a circle of tormenting foes, the circle diminishing all the time. While its attention was engaged by hyaenas on one side, three others stealthily approached the carcass from the other; they were intensely wary lest the lion should spring out on them; they were jumpy and the slightest movement in their direction made them retreat a few yards. They did not dare to go nearer and howled their annoyance. The howling and weird cackling increased and the lion roared back in a fury; all bedlam seemed to be let loose. This time the hyaenas didn't retreat, but dashed here and there with bewildering speed, just out of range of those deadly paws, and all the time the demon chorus was punctuated by the lion's roars. A hyaena crept in and managed to snatch a part of a leg from the carcass, and three others rushed after it to share the booty.

The rain came, and flashes of lightning stabbed the sky with light, picking out the clouds with an outline of fire. The whole scene was macabre. Suddenly, as if by magic, there was silence. Was the lame lion or the kill the main objective of the hyaenas' attack? It would not be the first lion to be killed by hyaenas.

The hyaenas closed their ranks again and formed a tight circle; the howling started and was intensified. The lion lunged forward time and time again and roared in anger, but the attackers were coming from all directions. Finally it could not stand it any longer and moved away from the bush. At once the hyaenas rushed in and dragged the carcass into the open. The lion was too preoccupied to stop them even if it could.

The carcass was a milling mass of hyaenas and the scrunch of bones was loud in our ears. We turned a spotlight on them and their eyes shone back like pairs of burning lights. But they took little notice of the beam; their main obsession was food and our presence was irrelevant to the situation. The lame lion was now some ten yards away from us with a few hyaenas still baiting it, but the main mass was on the carcass. We turned the headlights on and watched, fascinated, as the hyaenas fought for their share of the spoils. Then with dramatic suddenness the whole scene changed. There was a moment of complete silence; then from the darkness at our rear a lioness streaked into the lighted area followed by the rest of the pride. The hyaenas scattered to the four winds . . . one moment the carcass was a seething mass of them, the next it was a solitary pile of bones. The pride filed slowly past, victory had been achieved. We counted them in the light of the headlights . . . ten in all. The nearest pair of hyaena eyes was eighty yards away!

It had been a thrilling experience to be in the centre of such a drama! Had the pride responded to the roars of the lame lion and come to the rescue? Or was this too human an interpretation?

Whenever there was a buffalo killed by lions the head was retrieved, if possible, so that it could be examined by Michael Woodford for age and sex (the horns of the cow are longer and more slender). Research was in progress to see whether there was any selection by the lions. Did they choose the old or the young, the bulls or the cows, the diseased or the fit? Or was it a matter of chance?

It has been established in America that wolves are selective in their carabou kills, choosing the very young, or the old and diseased. Was it the same with lions? Not enough evidence is available at present to know the answer, but during our stay it was very noticeable that nearly always it was the bulls that were killed.

It is well known that the buffalo herd is a close social group and the individuals get protection from each other. When you approach a herd they will first run together and then turn round and face you, all heads pointing towards you. No pride of lions would stand a chance in the face of that kind of opposition.

However, when the bulls become old, they are expelled from the herd as other males become dominant. They live a solitary life, or more usually join up with a few other bulls, feeding in areas where the main herd seldom comes. Under these circumstances they become more vulnerable to attack. Many of the older animals are also subject to disease, especially tuberculosis, and no doubt this makes them much easier to kill. The females are not rejected from the herd in the same way and this may account for the fewer cows killed by lions.

The morning after the lame lion incident we returned to the kill to get the skull for examination. We found the spot where the kill had been made and the bush where the lame lion had sheltered, but there was no sign of the skull.

We searched methodically all over the area where the kill had been, but still no sign. It was quite mysterious how it had disappeared. Nothing could have eaten the large bones, however hungry or powerful!

About 400 yards away there was a hyaena den where we presumed the hyaenas had come from the previous night, so we went over to have a look at it. On the way we found the skull. In spite of the great weight and awkward shape it had been dragged 200 yards by the hyaenas towards their den. It brought home to us the tremendous strength of those animals.

Buffalo are not easy prey for lions. They are immensely strong and can do great damage with their horns, and lions have been gravely wounded or even killed by them.

A colleague witnessed an attack on a buffalo in daylight while we were there. The pride was moving slowly not far from a track when one of the lionesses saw a buffalo. It was one of four bulls isolated from the main herd, but it had moved away from the others. It did not appear to be a premeditated attack, but the lioness sprang on to its back and some of the pride joined in while the cubs crouched down motionless in the grass. Hearing the noise, the other bulls rushed to the victim and the lions were dislodged and gave up the attack. The presence of cars nearby may have been another reason why they desisted. We went out later to see if a kill had eventually been made, but there was no sign, and in this instance the buffalo had almost certainly escaped.

Buffalo are the main food of the lions in this part of the Park, although they supplemented the diet with any smaller prey they could find. Young wart-hogs were often killed and it is likely that lions before they become mature are their chief predators.

It appears that there is a definite relationship between the number of lions in a particular area and the number of large herbivores which make up their prey. It is usually found that the number killed each year is approximately the same as the number of herbivores born to the herds.

If the herds are not large enough to support the pride it will probably split up and some will move to hunting territories elsewhere. The average annual kill of ungulates by one lion has been estimated to range between twenty and thirty-six, so with a pride of over twenty animals the effect of predation on ungulate numbers is very considerable. Only very large herds of buffalo round Mweya could support so large a pride.

One evening we were going towards Katwe and met the pride coming along the main track towards us. We stopped and waited. A lioness was in the lead carrying what we thought was a newly born waterbuck in its mouth; it was still alive. The whole pride filed past on either side of us. One of the cubs had a long piece of thick wire in its mouth with which it had been playing, a change, no doubt, from playing with its mother's tail. There were fifteen of them, including the lame lion. They slowly wended their way over the hill towards the peninsula. It looked as if they were giving the Royal Circuit area a rest from their attentions and would attempt a kill on the peninsula.

Several times that night we heard them roaring some way below our house. It always followed the same pattern. One lion would start off, then others would join in, gradually reaching a climax of reverberating roars before dying away again to a low throaty afterthought by a single animal.

We expected to find a kill the next day, but there was no sign. No vultures were sitting in the trees or circling above. The herd of buffalo grazed as usual, apparently undisturbed, but the lions had not all left the area, for the lame lion and a lioness were seen lying up in the grass about 200 yards from our garden. They lazed the day away, and in the evening moved off the peninsula.

When lions were on the prowl in the late evening there were often two or three hyaenas following from a distance. There seemed to be a general pattern. Some hyaenas kept in touch with the lions, others regularly acted as scavengers in the Mweya district going round the gardens and raiding the dustbins, others were always to be seen near Hippo Pool and occasionally they all joined up when there was a good source of food to be exploited.

Towards the beginning of February the savannah was looking very dried up after a few weeks with little rain. The hippo were finding it particularly difficult to get enough grazing. Each night they had to go long distances, and in some cases it seemed that the energy expended in acquiring the food was more than they got back from the grass.

Some of them were in a poor way and we were not surprised when we found a dead one. It was floating feet upwards to one side of Hippo Pool and looked a grotesque sight in the moonlight. Two hyaenas were on the mud not far away. A very young baby hippo was nuzzling the carcass and wouldn't leave it. Presumably it was its mother that had died.

We were in the area looking for smaller carnivores for about an hour and a half and all that time the baby was by the dead animal. Other hippos were not far away, apparently unconcerned.

Returning the next afternoon to see what had happened, we found that the wind had blown the buoyant carcass across to the other side. Large numbers of vultures were flying round it and some were settled on the bare ground nearby. We thought we would try for a photograph and got as near as we could. It was a revolting spectacle to see the bloated body, feet in the air, rolling in the water, with the vultures trying to settle and vainly attempting to pierce the thick hide. So far it was intact.

While taking the photos we saw on the other side of the pool the pride of lions coming down to drink. It was a wonderful sight to see them in a long line led by a lioness. There were fifteen altogether, but no maned lions were with them. We quickly circled the pool once more to watch them more closely. Hippos were lazing in the water and Egyptian geese and various waders were scattered along the edge.

We parked quite near and watched them drinking – fifteen backs towards us in a tiny huddle as they drank. Thirst satisfied, they moved back a few yards and then basked in the sun, some facing the pool, others watching us, but completely at ease.

The heat was considerable as there was no shelter and the lions appeared to be feeling it too. Some elephants on the far side made their way to the water to drink as well.

After about a quarter of an hour the lions began to get more restive – a lioness and three nearly mature males with manes just starting to grow, got up and passed near the car. As they moved off the others began to stir. They had gone some way when the lioness stopped and scented the breeze; the smell of the dead hippo had arrested her attention and changing direction towards it she quickened her pace, the others following.

Anticipating their movements we made a big detour to arrive not far from the hippo, to watch for their coming. As the lions approached the vultures were put to flight in large numbers, but they soon flopped down again to continue their patient vigil.

The lions had a good look at the dead hippo from the edge, but it was too far out to reach so they lay down with the rest of the pride which had now arrived, getting what shade they could from the bushes.

The vultures meanwhile had made no impression on the dead animal. Large numbers waited on the ground quite near us; some stood, others squatted and had dust baths, a few spread their wings out displaying their white backs. The wind roughed up their coverts making them look like untidy bundles of feathers.

How long would this go on? Were they waiting for the hippo to burst with the pressure of the gases generated inside so that they would have a point of entry? It was a nasty thought, but from a vulture's point of view a useful solution to the problem. When we left they were still waiting patiently.

That night we passed the spot again. Already a number of hyaenas had collected; some were on shore and others were splashing about in the water near the dead animal. It was extraordinary to see the dancing reflections of their eyes as they swam round the body. Other hippos were near the dead one, making lunges at the hyaenas and apparently trying to keep them off. No hyaenas succeeded in feeding.

The following afternoon the vultures were at it again, but this time there was a difference. They were getting at the inside through some opening below the water line. It was astonishing to see these great birds putting their heads under the water to get at the entrails while they balanced on the carcass. One vulture savagely pecked the neck of another when its head was under water and a fight ensued, but no permanent damage was sustained.

Some hyaenas arrived long before dark and became very excited; they swam very well and dived repeatedly to snatch bits from the hippo, coming up at intervals to breathe and gulp down the revolting mouthfuls. The smell was nauseating, so we left them to their scavenging.

Hippos and hyaenas are very wary of each other, especially when the former have young with them. On one occasion when visiting Hippo Pool after dark we saw thirteen hyaenas towards one end of the grass-denuded flats; some were resting, others chasing each other and playing. One or two had something in their mouths, but we couldn't see what it was with the spotlight.

The focus of attention for some of them seemed to be a bush at the edge of the pool. Getting nearer we saw a group of hippos – several adults and at least four very young ones. They were faced on the shore side by a group of hyaenas moving excitedly here, there and everywhere.

The hippos came out of the water as a compact group; they were very wary, but appeared unafraid of the dancing hyaenas which let them pass and then closed in behind them. We could now see that they were less interested in the hippos than in the remains of something on the ground. When we got near it turned out to be the skull and some skin of a waterbuck, killed, presumably, by a lion at least two days before. It had long since ceased to be a supply of food, but was still a source of play to the younger hyaenas.

We became very intrigued by these hyaenas. What was their role in the savannah ecosystem? Was it primarily that of scavenger or was it carnivore? Hans Kruuk, working in the Serengeti, had made a brilliant study of their behaviour and was convinced that in that area they primarily acted as carnivores and were responsible for many game kills. In many instances he found that the lions then took over from the hyaenas, so the popularized concept of lions as predators and hyaenas as scavengers was reversed. There seems little doubt that both animals can play both roles, but in Queen Elizabeth Park the hyaena appeared to be more of a scavenger.

Hyaena Den, so called, by the side of the Kazinga Channel, was an interesting place. When we first investigated it in early January it was well used. Originally a complex of erosion gullies due to hippo overgrazing, it had been tunnelled into, and there were many entrances which were used by the hyaenas. Well-worn tracks led from some of these holes to the top of the slope, and most evenings you could find two or three hyaenas lazing about waiting for the sun to set.

There was a family born in one of these dens but it was difficult to know how many hyaenas were using the whole complex of holes and tunnels. Was it just the family or were most of the hyaenas in that district there?

By the end of January we were no longer seeing them in the evening when we passed the den, but we saw occasional animals not far away loping along the road about dusk, or later, usually going in the direction of Mweya. We thought we might try a dawn watch to see them come back. This might prove to be a better way of counting them.

We were up long before dawn and had to wake up the guards to unlock the gate out of Mweya. There was no moon and it was very dark as we went down Channel Track. We met a few hippos on their way back to the water and there was a herd of buffalo near the road a little farther on. There were no hyaenas about when we got near the den, but as it was not yet dawn we filled in the time by going on to Hippo Pool to see what was about. There were a lot of hippos there, as most of them had already gone back into the water and others were near the edge. A great grey mongoose ran across the track just beyond the pool, the tuft on its tail showing up clearly. We saw one hyaena there, but that was all.

When we saw the faintest glow in the east, we turned back and took up our position in readiness above Hyaena Den. The dawn chorus was very fine although the doves were somewhat monotonous – one bird persisted with its two-part song which was like a telephone bell continually ringing with nobody to lift the receiver.

No signs of hyaenas! We waited on hopefully. A fish eagle swooped in low and landed just below us on a *euphorbia*, and was followed soon after by an immature bird. The parent made its loud trumpeting cry, an arresting wild clarion call, but what a contrast when the juvenile did its best to follow suit! All it could do was to repeat a single note over and over again, however much it bent its head up and down in the process!

No hyaenas! This was surprising to us as we had assumed that they usually spent the day in their dens. We found later that the majority hid away in gullies or dense bushes, and only when breeding were you sure to find them in a particular den. When searching on foot for banded mongoose dens on the slopes above Lake Edward some time afterwards, we put up ten including a cub from a gully we were exploring, but there were no holes there for them to live in, and they were just sleeping rough.

The lions in the southern Ishasha region of the Park are famous for their habit of resting during the day in trees. On the first occasion that we saw them we had a small Volkswagen as our mode of transport. The area was very different from the bushy savannah round Mweya. It appeared much more 'park like' with its isolated fig trees and wide sweeps of comparatively short grass. Vast herds of topi and kob roamed this part of the Park, the former being killed by lions far more than the buffalo.

Searching for lions in trees can be rather like searching for a needle in a haystack, as there are so many trees, but certain ones were well known as habitual favourites, as they had short trunks and big boughs which spread out more or less parallel to the ground. One of the fig trees contained three lionesses. They were straddled about in various attitudes with their legs dangling down and their bodies supported by various boughs. They didn't look particularly comfortable, but one was dozing with its head resting against a convenient branch. It was surprising how difficult they were to see from thirty yards away.

One of the advantages of this tree-resting habit is that the animal is not only in the shade, but the air is able to circulate all round its body more effectively than when on the ground, thus helping to keep it cool.

I manœuvred the car round the tree to get a better position for photography, keeping my eyes on the lions, and got the hind wheel into a wart-hog hole! It was not the best position in which to be stuck. The hole was not deep, but the sides were too steep for the wheel to grip! If lions could be credited with a sense of humour, this would have been the moment to have shown it, but as it was they appeared to show little interest. The nearest lioness was about fifteen feet away, the others were in higher branches. It might have been several hours before they moved off!

I decided to test their reactions by getting out on the far side, holding the door in readiness to get back if it moved from its slumbering position. I got out. The lioness opened an eye and immediately got up to a standing position on the big bough on which she was lying and I shot back into the car. But it was a false alarm. She had not liked my nearness and was moving to a branch higher up in the tree. I got out again and there was no further movement. There were three of us in the car and while two of us rocked it from the strategic side (the door being kept open) and pushed, Betty drove and the car just got clear. We got back quite relieved that we hadn't to wait until the lions condescended to go off.

Another visit to Ishasha provided us with no problems, but we saw the lions again. This time there was only a single old lioness in the fig tree, but underneath a neighbouring tree was a large male lion with a lioness flat on her side nearby. The lion was very alert and by his behaviour it seemed that we had disturbed a courting couple. When the car got near, he roared and charged forward a couple of yards, but then hesitated, lashing his tail furiously. We decided it was courteous to leave them to each other.

The same day we did a round of the forest bordering the Ishasha river. This river forms the boundary between Uganda and Congo and we watched with interest a very nervous herd of elephant crossing the river from the forest beyond. The game animals were certainly no respecters of political boundaries.

It was here that we saw our first giant forest hog. We came on it suddenly, a very large male. It stood and stared for a few seconds before dashing off, giving us a fleeting chance of a photograph. We followed hopefully and were lucky enough to see the rest of the family, the sow and three hoglets, but they quickly disappeared into the forest.

They were very different from wart-hogs, being much bigger, very hairy and with more cylindrical bodies. The large boar looked black compared with the grey of a wart-hog, and the grotesque swellings on its face below the eyes and the wicked-looking tusks were most impressive. He was quite a formidable beast! It was good to have had such fine views of a species which had only been 'discovered' in 1904.

Returning through the Maramagambo, we were travelling quite fast when we came to a long straight stretch of road. In the distance were two dark objects by the side of the road which I thought were roadmen, as we had seen others previously, but they didn't seem quite right. On looking through the binoculars I saw they were chimpanzees, a mother and her young one. We got quite near before the infant jumped on the back of its mother and they both disappeared quickly into the forest. This was the first time we had seen wild chimpanzees. Two new species in one day was something to remember!

We were still anxious to learn more about the behaviour of lions at a kill at night. Our experience with the lame lion had ended abruptly when the rest of the pride had returned. Since then we had not found any buffalo kills. Apparently the pride had been in another part of their territory or had been feeding on smaller prey such as wart-hogs, which had been eaten quickly.

Our chance came when we happened to catch sight of a lone lioness in the late afternoon, moving between some bushes near the marshy area beyond Hippo Pool. Going over to investigate, we found the rest of the pride round the carcass of a buffalo. It had probably been killed that morning because already two or three lions were lying on the grass having had their fill, but at least ten were still attacking the carcass with vigour. At this stage the buffalo's head and most of the limbs were untouched and the rib case was just exposed and the contents were being eaten. There would be no chance for hyaenas for some time, but we thought it was worth coming back at dusk to see what happened after that.

It was nearly dark when we manœuvred the Land-Rover to a spot about five yards from the nearest lions, turned on the lights, and settled down to watch. The pride took no notice of us in spite of our nearness to them. Most of them were still vigorously tearing at the carcass; five or six were trying to sleep off their excesses, draped across the grass in various attitudes of abandon. One lioness flopped down by our front wheel and promptly went to sleep.

The lake flies were a great nuisance that night as the lights attracted them. They were in dense clouds round the headlights and periodically we had to switch off to disperse them. When turned on again, they collected in a few moments. Each fly made its own spiral flight and caught in the light they made a fantastic pattern of movement; thousands of weaving lights forming an ever-changing geometrical design bounded by the blackness of the night.

We took flashlight pictures of the lions after allowing a decent interval for the lake flies to disperse. The lions went on with the feast oblivious of the flies and our flash bulbs. Some were licking the meat off the ribs with their rough tongues, making loud rasping noises, others were gnawing at the legs. There were deep growlings and occasional outbursts of louder roars when one lion forgot its feline manners. Using a long papyrus stick we had brought for the purpose, we tied the microphone to the end of it and held it as near the lions as possible as they continued their meal. It made a particularly intimate tape recording of their table talk! They took no notice at all of the device.

We turned the headlights off and listened in the darkness to the scrunching of bones a few yards away. We ate some bananas to keep them company! In the darkness we saw no lake flies, of course, but instead the fireflies over the marsh gave a spectacular display. Their flight patterns by contrast were quite at random and no individual could be followed for long, as its luminous organ was periodically switched off.

The night wore on, but no hyaenas turned up. Periodically we would use the spotlight and scan the countryside for eye reflections, but apart from a single hyaena, perhaps seventy yards away, they appeared to be uninterested in the kill.

It looked as if the lions would be there all night, for as soon as one retired to rest another would wake up and take its place; the general pattern was the same as we had witnessed before. Rather than stop up all night we decided to get a little sleep and return at dawn to see the sequel.

On the way home as we passed Hippo Pool we saw ten hyaenas in the vicinity of the dead hippo. This was obviously why we had not seen them before round the kill.

It was a short night for us, but when we returned soon after dawn, there was the pride, all fifteen animals, lying on the bare ground near the edge of Hippo Pool. They must have left the kill, had a drink and were now resting. We found the last remains of the buffalo being vigorously attacked by a large flock of vultures. They were tearing at the remnants of flesh between the ribs and fighting for possession of the larger pieces.

It was interesting that no hyaenas had taken over when the lions left, but presumably they had been too preoccupied by the hippo meat. We severed the head from the vertebrae with an axe and brought it back to Michael Woodford for ageing. The final rite had been performed.

CHAPTER FIVE

The Forest Regions

The forest region was an irresistible attraction, although strictly speaking it was irrelevant to the main project with which we were engaged. It made an exciting break from routine work on the savannah, interesting though that was, and although we had little time to do more than study it superficially it was nevertheless rewarding to us.

The main forest region of the Park was the Maramagambo, an immense area of rain forest straddling the road to Ishasha and becoming denser the nearer it got to the escarpment in the east, where the rainfall was greatest.

We were also able to visit the fascinating Budongo Forest which is famous for its chimpanzees. It lies south of the Murchison Falls National Park. A rather different kind of forest was seen on the slopes of the Ruwenzori; although similar in many respects, it was really montane forest and its vegetation changed very much with altitude. An even more exciting montane forest was the Impenetrable Forest of S.W. Uganda which we passed through on our way to Kisoro and the Birungo Volcanoes of that region.

The trouble with forests is the difficulty in penetrating them. In the Maramagambo there was one good road that passed through its western edge, and a few tracks which enabled you to get to its north-east corner, otherwise it meant going on foot. However, towards the end of our stay, a track was being cut which led several miles into otherwise inaccessible forest, and this proved to be an exciting mode of entry.

Our first visits were to the region of the Maramagambo near the Nyamusingire Lake to the north-east of the forest. This meant taking the Land-Rover across on the ferry and taking the track to the main Congo road. Crossing the road we got into a rough track which led to a woodman's camp at the edge of the forest.

A river ran through the forest near the camp. Its banks were thickly clothed in forest trees and on one there was a large collection of open-

23. Elephant scenting

24. Recognition by bull elephant of newly-born calf

25. Lions feeding at a buffalo kill (by flashlight)

26. Spotted hyaenas at the remains of a lion kill (by flashlight)

27. White-backed vultures

28. Bull buffalo and family of Egyptian geese

29. Lion pride resting by Hippo Pool

30. Elephants at Hippo Pool

billed storks. The curious thing about this medium-sized, all-black stork is the bill. When the mandibles are tightly shut at the tip you can still see daylight through the middle part, a very convenient shape for crushing snails. We had seen some previously at Pelican Point, but not in such numbers.

Before entering the forest proper we saw a large group of baboons of all ages. They were shy and soon went to cover, but being extremely inquisitive some climbed trees to get a better view of us and others stood up as tall as possible to see over the long grass.

As we followed the track slowly through the forest the trees became taller and more impressive. Some of the older trees had curious cabbage-like plants growing epiphytically on their boughs; strangely enough, these were a species of fern in spite of their superficial likeness to cabbages.

We hunted on either side of the track, and Betty discovered a most curious flower emerging from a mass of fallen leaves on the forest floor. It was orange-red and had a large number of stiff petals forming a beautiful geometrical pattern. Superficially it reminded us of a large everlasting flower, although it did not belong to the same family. It had no leaves, and ants were all over it, feeding on the nectar. We found out later that it was a plant called Thonningia, which is a root parasite. In West Africa, apparently, these flowers are tied to the ankles of small children when they are learning to walk. It is also said to have therapeutic properties and is used by Africans to cure eczema.

Many of the trees had curious, large, dark swellings on them, which were the nests of tree termites. These insects play an important role in the ecology of the forest as they remove much of the dead wood.

While we were searching for plants and insects, there was a crashing near the top of the trees and a black and white colobus monkey made a great leap to another tree across the track; another followed it and then several others. When they looked down on us we could see their black and white faces and magnificent long tails. They made a quick get-away, but we heard them for some time as they noisily leapt from tree to tree, keeping high up in the canopy.

Our main purpose that day was to visit a cave in the heart of the forest where thousands of fruit bats were said to roost. As this meant walking for some distance we asked a Ranger to accompany us. It was as well we did as the cave was not easy to find. The Ranger and his companion were both armed in case we met a buffalo which turned awkward.

We left the track at a high vantage point where we could see below us the great expanse of the forest. At first we had to get through a region of tall grass, higher than our heads. We worked our way in single file down the steep slope. With the grass so tall all round us we realized how relatively useless sight must be to most animals living in situations such as these and how scent and hearing were all important.

Soon we entered the forest, following a poorly discernible path among the trees. Some of the trees were a great height with fine buttresses at the base. The forest floor had little vegetation, but was covered with a carpet of dead leaves. Light came through weak and dappled.

We struggled on past a river which could be seen far below looking strangely green and sinister, as little light reached it through the thick canopy. The going was not too easy, but the Ranger knew exactly the best route, and we twisted and turned between the great trunks avoiding the thickest vegetation.

It was very hot and humid and there was no wind. Stopping for a moment we realized how silent everything was except the distant noise of the river and the calls of a few birds high up in the tree tops.

After half a mile or so we smelt a strange pungent odour, at first very faint, and then all-pervading. Stopping, we heard a high-pitched hissing sound coming from somewhere below us. At first we could see nothing, but going nearer the edge of a ravine, we looked down to see the mouth of a cave. Loud noises were coming from it and a number of large bats were flying about near the entrance.

We clambered down the side of the ravine and an extraordinary sight met our eyes. The cave was really a large tunnel open at both ends and hanging from the roof and sides were tens of thousands of bats.

The cave was about fifteen feet high and went back about forty. Every niche was crammed with hanging fruit bats. We cautiously entered the cave and hundreds more took to flight and whirled around us. In spite of the restricted space no bat hit us or collided with another and on every side they were peeling off from their perches and joining the throng. The noise was almost deafening as they all joined in protest, making their high-pitched squeaks.

The smell was almost overpowering, and the droppings on the floor made an oozy carpet over the loose boulders. It was impossible to estimate their numbers, but there must have been fifty thousand at least. More and more were fluttering about near the cave entrance looking for places to settle, and soon the surrounding trees were festooned with clusters of them hanging upside down.

They were rousette fruit bats, one of the only species of African fruit bat to roost in caves. Most species, like the straw-coloured fruit bat, roost in trees; we saw a fine colony of these in eucalyptus trees in the centre of Kampala. The rousette is a dark greyish-brown bat of medium size. There was one albino specimen in the cave; it looked so strange, along with all the others, with its off-white fur and pink eyes.

It was astonishing to see such a vast concentration of animals in one small area; the food they consumed each night must have been very great. At first sight, the middle of a dense tropical forest was such an improbable place to find a great colony of bats, but feeding on fruit, this was undoubtedly a strategic place to be. The numbers of species of trees in a tropical forest is very great and many of these bear edible fruits. They ripen at different seasons and a winged animal is well adapted to search out and exploit each source of food as it becomes available.

On the way back we found the going harder as it was mainly uphill and sweat poured off us. We saw more flowers of the strange parasite, thonningia, among the dead leaves while keeping our eyes open for animal tracks. Blue Duiker must have been quite common because although we did not see any we kept coming across their droppings, which looked like a pile of shiny blackcurrants.

On another occasion we explored the more southerly part of the forest. On our way, after crossing the ferry we saw numbers of red-collared widow birds fluttering like butterflies over the tall grasses. They were most peculiar to watch as they had very short wings and an immensely long tail, which either trailed or fanned out to show three parts. The males were black all over except for the red patch on the upper chest.

As the main road traversed the edge of the forest we once more saw a chimpanzee beside the road, but it had slipped into the forest by the time we got there. Once you have seen one, they are quite unmistakable as they appear so intensely black, even from a distance.

We turned off the road on to the new track, which was, by then, not nearly finished, but it penetrated the forest at least five miles. The going was still extremely rough, but it gave us a chance to get some distance into one of the wildest parts of the Maramagambo.

At first the trees were short, but as we penetrated farther they got taller and taller. There were a lot of flame trees in full bloom which were a magnificent sight. Usually, in the forest, you can only see these from above; from below, all you see is a carpet of fallen flowers, but with the cutting of the track we could occasionally get good views of the trees, especially when there was a steep slope.

The butterflies were spectacular. They, too, are usually at the tops of the trees and seldom seen, but in the clearings they came down lower and we saw them well. Many of them were swallowtails; some black with green bands, others with blue; very large lemon yellow ones with black patterns, others were deeper orange. They floated majestically in and out of the trees and settled occasionally. One bush was covered in flowers and this had attracted dozens of these lovely swallowtails.

A very dark brown butterfly was common in the shady regions; when it settled on the mud its colour blended admirably. There were several species of hairstreak butterfly flitting from tree to tree. When settled, they moved their hind wings independently of their fore, in a way characteristic of most of that family.

It started to rain quite gently and under these conditions they were much easier to approach and photograph. When the rain increased many of them disappeared to shelter higher up among the foliage, but a burst of sun soon after brought them floating down like coloured leaves to the more open spaces.

Wet mud or puddles attracted the butterflies in great numbers, especially where there had been dung to increase the nitrogen content of the water. In one place we found literally hundreds of pierids settled on the moist mud and several dozen swallowtails imbibing the fluid. It was possible to approach within a few feet as they were so engrossed in their feeding. The water was continually being absorbed through the proboscis, passed right through the body and excreted at the anus as a continuous succession of drops. The various dissolved substances of nutritive value were presumably being absorbed as the water went through. As the solution was so dilute, a great volume of water had to pass through to obtain sufficient nutrients. One swallowtail was so intent on its drinking that it took no notice when a smaller species settled on its closed wings as if it were a flower.

We were fascinated by a small species of dragonfly which flew up and down the track. When it settled it chose the tips of bare twigs. It had large dark patches on the wings and after settling it moved its wings backwards and downwards in a series of jerks and at the same time protruded its head and body. The result was the appearance of a dead flower or fruit at the end of the twig. It was extremely deceptive.

We saw some interesting birds, but usually we only just caught glimpses of them. The most striking were the black-and white-casqued hornbills, which had a most laboured flight as if it were a great effort to get their heavy bills off the ground. They were the commonest hornbill of the forest, easily distinguished by the black and white plumage and black and white casque on the bill.

One of the most beautiful birds we saw was a blue-breasted kingfisher which flew along our track. It was larger and brighter than the woodland kingfisher we had seen near Mweya, and the pale but vivid blue showed up beautifully against the black on the wings as it caught the sun.

An even more brilliant species of spectacular size, was the great blue turaco. All the turacos are spectacular, but this was the finest of them all. We first caught sight of it as a flash of blue high up among the foliage, but, as we waited quietly, it flew to a better position for viewing and we could see its fine crest and very long blue and yellow tail. It was a glorious bird to see in the sunshine.

The only bird of prey we saw in the forest was a buzzard; we identified it as a mountain buzzard, but we couldn't see it quite well enough to be certain. In spite of its name, this is a forest species, although it is probably more common in montane forests.

As we slowly made our way farther into the forest we met two troupes of baboon. They were more inquisitive than frightened when we approached, but were content to view us from a distance. Several mothers had babies with them and one appeared to be newly born. We also came across the largest troupe of colobus we had seen; there were probably about twenty. This time we were able to follow them some way into the forest and watch their magnificent acrobatics. They kept to the taller trees and we never saw any descend to the ground.

It began to get rather dark and rain started to fall, so we had lunch in the Land-Rover. Suddenly without any warning there was a sizzling flash of lightning and simultaneously a tremendous crash of thunder. Coming without warning it was very frightening, but it prepared us somewhat for the next few claps and the torrential rain that followed. The suddenness of the storm was most remarkable. Fortunately it did not last long and although the track got very wet we managed to negotiate the inclines without too much difficulty, but it prevented us going as far in as we should have liked.

Returning by the main road in the late afternoon we saw by one of the bridges a tremendous gathering of baboons. There must have been at least seventy-five. Some were on the road, others on the bank of the stream and the majority on a grassy patch by the edge of the forest. When we got near, those on the road fled, some jumped the river, others landed short with a splash and clambered up the bank looking rather bedraggled. Once safe on the other side they lost their fear and we were able to watch them. Every member of baboon society was represented and it looked as if several troupes had combined temporarily to make such a large group.

We looked for an opportunity to visit the same area again, but at night. I wanted a tape recording of the various forest sounds at dusk. Unfortunately the weather was becoming much more unsettled and the forest area was subjected to repeated thunderstorms. The track was so muddy after rain that few days were suitable. One evening we tried our luck, and taking supper with us reached the new track about three-quarters of an hour before dark. We managed the first quarter of a mile as that was fairly level, but got well and truly bogged down on the first proper slope. We managed to turn round at the bottom of the incline, but in spite of four-wheel drive and low ratio gears we made little progress. Darkness fell, but with the help of a torch we cut masses of vegetation with a panga to give a grip to the wheels and foot by foot we made the ascent, forcing wooden poles behind the wheels to prevent them sliding back each time. We were weary, caked in mud but triumphant when, after an hour and a half's toil we eventually got back to the main road to have our supper of hard-boiled eggs. Taking the shells off was a revolting business with all that mud, but they tasted good all the same!

Another rain forest we visited was the Budongo. We had seen chimpanzees in the Maramagambo, but only for fleeting moments and we greatly wanted to see them properly. Some years ago, Vernon Reynolds had studied them for ten months in the Budongo and we knew there were a number of groups there which could sometimes be seen. The difficulty was that they moved about extensively and you could never be sure where they would be. Like the fruit bats of the Maramagambo, chimpanzees are fruit eaters. They know all the best fruit trees in their area and visit them according to their time of ripening. When fruit is in abundance in one place a lot of chimpanzees may be seen together, but this chance does not come very often.

Mr Baggerley has a guest house on the road that cuts through the forest, and we arranged to stop there for a few nights while we were looking for chimps. We also intended to visit Murchison Falls National Park over the same period.

We reached the guest house after a long, hot, and dusty journey. The garden was like a haven of peace with its green lawns, flowering trees and varied assortment of bougainvillaeas.

We were introduced at once to the most important guest in the house – a four-month-old chimpanzee! It had been picked up as an abandoned infant in the forest nearby and was being brought up like a human baby. It was a charming creature and full of character. It had been named Beaverbrook! When we saw it, it was wearing a nappie, hugging a favourite towel and trying spasmodically to play on a typewriter.

That evening after dark we took a walk along one of the tracks into the forest to get the atmosphere of the place. The trees looked very impressive in the clear moonlight, their great straight trunks leading upwards to a splendid canopy above. Those with tiny leaves made a lace-like tracery across the sky, which was very beautiful. There was an incessant chorus of crickets and as we passed a wetter area the voices of hundreds of frogs and toads were added to the din. Then we heard a weird screaming which was answered far over by some more. They were tree hyraxes without doubt. We got quite near to one, but they were remarkably ventriloquistic and difficult to locate and our torch failed to reflect their eyes. But it was interesting to have heard them as they did not occur in the Maramagambo. They are said to sleep in holes by day, far above the ground, and at night explore the large boughs and trunks, climbing vertically if necessary with the help of adhesive organs on the soles of their feet, which produce a partial vacuum; a wonderful arboreal adaptation.

The next morning was beautifully sunny and clear after a shower in the night. Vervet monkeys were playing in one of the trees in the garden and sunbirds were delicately sipping nectar from the flowers as they hovered like humming-birds in front of each. Our main objective that morning was to see the chimps and our guide was a young Ugandan who knew the forest well and was a good tracker. He came with us in the car along the forest road, stopping periodically to listen, as chimpanzees are noisy creatures at times and their cries are the best clues to their whereabouts. We could hear nothing, but our guide seemed confident that they were not very far away. When we had parked he cut sticks for each of us to help beat down the undergrowth and in single file we entered the forest, our guide leading the way with his panga.

At first he went slowly, pausing constantly to listen, and it was not long before we heard the chimpanzees in the far distance. The forest contained some immense trees and the undergrowth was sufficiently thick to make the going difficult. We walked through large patches of ground orchids, over dead tree trunks and through mud. In places the ground was carpeted with dead leaves or the fruits and flowers from the trees above us. Lianas were cut to make a possible path and anything spiney cut back; we dodged under or round the larger obstacles or slowly hacked our way through. As the noises of the chimpanzees grew louder so our guide increased his pace.

Eventually we reached a place which smelt heavily of chimpanzees, and looking up we saw some of their beds high up in the trees. Their dung was scattered about on the ground and it was obvious that they had been there the night before.

It was impossible to go quietly at the pace the guide was setting, but he knew what he was doing, and suddenly he signed to us to stop. We looked up through the undergrowth and there was a young chimp high up in one of the trees! As we waited quietly to restore their confidence after our noisy approach we could hear others around us, but it was difficult to catch sight of them through all the vegetation. Edging forward very quietly we got into a better position for viewing, and there they were silhouetted against the sky. They were in a very tall tree which had great bunches of fruit hanging from its upper branches. More came into view, and soon we were watching eight of them busily feeding on the fruits, after selecting the ripe ones with great care. They had obviously had a good meal already and it was not long before some of the adults started to clean themselves and groom each other's fur. One went to sleep on a branch. Then suddenly, as if at a signal, they all became alert and a tremendous din broke out, the forest ringing with their weird hollow cries. The noise stopped as abruptly as it had started and we heard in the distance the replies of another band far away. It seemed to be their method of keeping in touch.

We rested between the buttresses of a huge mahogany tree as we watched them having their siesta, but after a time there was a general movement by three or four of them, and swinging from branch to branch with easy grace they moved away to other trees. They were the true masters of the forest. It had been a wonderful experience to have seen them so close without causing them to panic. We crept quietly away.

We also made trips to the montane forest of the Ruwenzori, but through lack of time were unable to explore it as much as we would have liked. It was possible to take a Land-Rover quite high above the copper mining town of Kalembe by a track that zigzagged up the mountains to about seven thousand feet. It led to a water supply station for the mines. A Ugandan flagged us down and we gave him a lift. He had a fine fur hat which looked rather distinguished and we gathered that he had made it from the skins of tree hyraxes, which were not uncommon in the mountains. Their cousins, the rock hyaenas, are the coneys of the Bible. They are allied, not to rabbits, but to the hoofed animals and are, in fact, distant relatives of the elephant!

When the road ended we followed the track upwards on foot and were able to examine the montane vegetation. The forest largely consisted of broad-leaved trees of many species, some reaching considerable heights. Some were heavily parasitized by a species of mistletoe and a few had epiphytic orchids hanging from their mossy boughs. Tree ferns in great numbers added grace and beauty to the scene and here and there were giant lobelias sending their spikey inflorescences up to fifteen feet from the ground. Creepers twined round the tree trunks and tough lianas festooned the spaces between them. Everything was very green and very moist.

At ground level great carpets of mosses flourished on the wet humus and liverworts with their umbrella-like sporangiophores looked like a forest of miniature palm trees when you stooped down to their level. Balsams grew luxuriantly under these damp conditions, those with various shades of pink were the most common, but there was also a smaller flowered species with intensely deep purplish-blue petals which was most attractive. A large splash of red among the rank vegetation turned out on closer inspection to be an out-sized fire lily. It had a spherical head of flowers about five inches in diameter on a three-foot stalk swathed in large leaves, a magnificent button-hole for somebody!

On the surface of a large leaf was a curious dark red object which looked like a rough-shelled limpet. It was hard to believe that it was a living animal until six legs appeared from underneath and it started to move. It was, in fact, a magnificently camouflaged 'tortoise' beetle. When it moved to the edge of the leaf, the two closely-fitting elytra unfolded, and spreading them out like a ladybird it unfolded its wings and flew off. It was a remarkable transformation from inanimate to animate!

Going higher, the trees gradually thinned out and we reached the bamboo zone at between eight and nine thousand feet. Beyond were the higher peaks, but the very highest, which are always snow-covered, were not visible from where we were.

On our way down again we found safari ants crossing the track. They formed a thick meandering black line. A long thick bamboo had been chosen as part of their route and thousands of these fearsome ants were clinging to it, while others carried larvae and pupae along the trail. Soldier ants with huge jaws scouted on either side of the column and climbed anything in their path. Photographing them in close-up was a hazardous procedure as our legs were very vulnerable to their attentions and their bites were painful.

Birds were not easy to see amongst so much vegetation but they made a lot of noise. The most arresting was a series of raucous 'kar, kar, kars'. We traced them to a group of black-billed turacos; large green birds with beautiful red patches on the primaries which were most conspicuous when they flew. Unlike most turacos we saw, the crest on this species was inconspicuous.

We made one visit to the Ituri rain forest west of the Ruwenzori, a vast area untouched by civilization, which stretched a great distance into the Congo. The forest to us was more memorable for its human inhabitants than for the animals we saw there.

We reached it from Fort Portal through the magnificent Buranga pass which cuts through the northern part of the Ruwenzori. The road finally descends by a series of hairpin bends to the Bwamba region and peters out some fifteen miles farther on at Bundibugyo; after that, nothing but wild inaccessible country.

The Bwamba and Ituri forests are the home of the pygmies. On our return from Bundibugyo, our only source of petrol for forty miles, we were passing through the wild spectacular forest region when a group of pygmies rushed out of the forest waving and gesticulating and barring our way. When we stopped, others joined them until there were about twenty all round the car. They tried to sell us colobus skins, pygmy lutes and bows decorated with monkey fur. One of them could speak a little English and we gathered amidst the hubbub the prices they were demanding. Needless to say, the prices were exorbitant, but we agreed to buy two of their wares, largely to keep them quiet. Unfortunately, Betty misjudged their mood and took a snapshot through the windscreen. At once they demanded more and more money and became most aggressive and threatening. One brandished a short club-like stick and others large stones which seemed to appear from nowhere. We had no intention of being forced to pay the huge sums they were demanding and clearly it was time to go. As I started the engine one man hit Betty on the side of the face and she quickly put up the window to protect herself, but clearly the incident had been planned because some had taken up a position in the road some yards in front and stood there with large stones ready to hurl at the car.

As I accelerated towards them I heard the window being shattered and we were covered in pieces of broken glass, but I had to keep my eye on those in front so as not to run them down. Luckily one great stone which hit the windscreen glanced off the sloping surface, and being laminated glass it did not shatter.

We stopped a mile on and surveyed the damage; three side windows of the car were completely shattered and the windscreen was cracked! Glass was all over the car and we found a stone the size of a tennis ball inside, which we kept as a memento.

We were unhurt, but it had been a somewhat alarming experience. It had happened so quickly that our dominant emotion had been surprise more than fright. As we were cleaning up the mess and getting the glass out of our clothes a Land-Rover of the Uganda Police arrived and they heard our story. They told us that this sort of thing had happened before and a police escort was necessary on this road. It would have been helpful to have known that before!

Most of the Ituri pygmies are said to be friendly people, but unfortunately those on the edge of the forest had become spoiled and corrupted and their greed for what money could buy had made them a menace to anybody who ventured along that road.

CHAPTER SIX

The Banded Mongoose Investigation

It was not until we had spent six or seven weeks studying the ecology of the Park and looking for the middle-sized carnivores that we decided to concentrate on the banded mongoose. The main factor that decided us was the discovery of a den where they were living, but the fact that they were diurnal was another important reason, as our time was limited and we had no radio-telemetry to follow up our work on the nocturnal ones, a requisite we thought was almost essential if their dens were to be found.

It was not long after our arrival that we first saw banded mongooses. We were being initiated into the art of doing a game count in the peninsula region. The technique was to cover the whole area by Land-Rover by taking a series of parallel courses up and down the peninsula trying not to disturb the game sufficiently to move them into a region not yet counted. An exactly parallel course was not easy in bushy savannah where the more open spaces may contain wallows and wart-hog holes, but by taking a more or less similar route each time the inaccuracies of the count were reduced.

On rounding some bushes we suddenly saw them – brown shapes in the long grass running to avoid the vehicle. One stood up to get a better view before dashing into the bushes. It was difficult to count them in the long grass, but there were at least twelve. They had gone as quickly as they had appeared.

They were most attractive animals to look at. The adults reach a length of about two feet including an eight to ten inch tail. When seen in open country they look like a pack of miniature otters in the wrong habitat, with heads near the ground, their hindquarters curiously humped and their tails tapering. The general colour is dark brown, but the shoulders are often grizzled grey. The top of the head is dark, almost black in some, but the nose is pink and the lower half of the head a much lighter brown. The eyes are small, dark and beady and the ears rounded and close to the body. Only the hind part of the body is banded, the pattern being due to alternate darker and lighter bands which seem to go in and out like a concertina as the animals hunch themselves up or stretch. The legs are nearly black and when they stand up with their front legs dangling they look as if they are wearing long black gloves. An adult weighs four or five pounds.

They belong to the family *Viverridae* which also includes civet sand genets and of course the other species of mongoose.

Although we saw packs of these active carnivores at various times, they took fright very easily, and we were not able to observe them for long enough to find out much about them. The crucial question was where they lived. If only we could find where they were breeding this would be a focal point for observations and we might get somewhere.

Hinton and Dunn (1967) state that 'Sometimes an entire colony takes refuge in a rock shelter or warren with only one or two entrances. In local sandy country, whether open or wooded, they live in ordinary warrens. The burrows are usually concealed under clumps of bush.' Shortridge (1934) described how one colony inhabited the crevices of an old stone weir, and Heller (1911) described how they 'do not stop long in any locality, but take up a temporary abode in any nest of burrows which they find convenient. They do not remain for more than a day or so in any one sort of burrow.'

We quartered large areas of savannah in the Land-Rover, looking for possible hide-outs, and concentrating on regions where we had seen packs previously. The only termite mounds with holes in them that we could discover had been made by wart-hogs, or were quite plainly disused. We came across no sets of small burrows and although we examined large numbers of clumps of bushes we found no traces.

It looked as if Heller was right and the packs were wandering all over the place and resting in thick cover each night, pursuing an almost nomadic existence. But they had to breed somewhere, and we had already seen packs containing very small animals which could only have been a month or two old. What kind of shelter did they use for breeding?

During the course of our searching we were on the look out for any clues such as the presence of dung, but what was banded mongoose dung like? Odd scats of about the right size were found in various places, sometimes on the ground, sometimes on termite mounds, but these were more likely to have belonged to the more solitary species.

You would expect a lot of scats in one area for a species which travelled in a pack.

On one occasion we visited the main hyaena den and looked around for clues of occupation. Hyaena dung is of large diameter and usually very whitish due to the high proportion of bone eaten. We found only old scats with this appearance, but in one place there were a lot of fresh ones, blackish in colour and distinctly smaller. On closer inspection they obviously contained insect remains and this seemed out of context for hyaenas. Civet was a possibility as we knew this species habitually used the same area for defaecation: we could not be sure. We dusted the dung with fine earth so that we could see the next day if any fresh had appeared.

There was rain in the night so this gave us a chance to see footprints plainly. We found plenty of hyaena prints, but there was no fresh dung and no prints of any smaller animal nearby. So we were no further forward.

A few days later we were talking with the Park Engineer and his wife who were both very interested in and knowledgeable about the African fauna. They told us that some six weeks before they had come across a termite mound with banded mongooses going in and out. This was encouraging, and they kindly agreed to show us the place.

It meant a long detour to get the vehicles near the spot, but after a short search on foot the mound was discovered. It was on a slope sparsely dotted with clumps of bushes and at the bottom of the valley was a gully full of dense bushes and trees which led towards the Kazinga Channel.

The mound had some bushes behind it which gave some cover and there were three entrances about $4\frac{1}{2}''$ in diameter, two at the base and one towards the back, higher up. What was so interesting to us was the vast number of droppings that covered the mound and the flat area in front of it, and in fact for several yards around. This dung was exactly the same as we had previously seen at the hyaena den! There was no mistaking it, with its concentrated remains of dung beetle elytra and millipede segments.

The whole mound had a musky odour and by the appearance of the dung it certainly looked as if it was being occupied. To make sure we got some stiff grass stalks and put them vertically across the entrances; if they were moved next day we should know the mound was being used.

Knowing what to look for now, we decided to call at the hyaena den on the way back to see if there were holes anywhere near the dung we had seen there previously. On arrival we could see no fresh dung, but in a gully nearby there were several holes of the right diameter and it was clear that these had been used recently. We suspected that a pack of bandeds had been there, but it was now abandoned. We put sticks across the holes to make sure, and left.

The following day we spent in the Maramagambo Forest and had no chance to visit the newly found mongoose den, but the next day we were delighted to find that our grass stems had been dislodged and there was more fresh dung.

The next problem was how to watch the den. We took the Land-Rover across the opposite hillside and tried to get through the scrub in the gully, but it was too dense. Eventually we found we could skirt the gully and get to a position below the den from which we could watch it. We thought if we could back the vehicle on to a bush we should be less conspicuous and if we got there well before they came back after their day's foraging, they would probably take little notice. We trimmed some of the larger grasses in front of the den so that we could get an uninterrupted view, but refrained from going too near in case our scent should frighten them when they returned later in the day. The plan was to watch that evening. Betty and I would take up a position about thirty-five yards from the den in the Land-Rover and Andrew in another vehicle would watch with a telescope from the opposite hillside. In this way we hoped that he would pick up the pack long before they came into view and we could compare notes later.

We arrived at 5.20, more than two hours before dark, and carefully backed the Land-Rover against the bush. A violent wind was blowing from the S.E. and it was overcast and not very promising. We kept scanning the hillside with binoculars, but very little was stirring. At 6.30 we saw two dark shapes in the long grass and thought at first they might be birds, but then we saw their heads peeping through the grass and scenting suspiciously. They were bandeds all right! They came forward slowly, their heads going up and down repeatedly as they scented the air. Others were behind them, and, as they got nearer, the grass seemed to be alive with them, their bands showing up beautifully in the evening sunlight which had just burst through.

They approached the den in single file, but on reaching it all bunched together and looked hard at us, all scenting, all very alert. They were clearly very puzzled, but were not obviously frightened. To our relief they soon became more at ease and went in and out of the holes and climbed over the mound; one very young one slithered down one side and nestled beside an adult. Most of them were huddled together on the bare patch in front of the mound, but a very large animal lay on the top with its chin resting on the surface. A juvenile rolled sideways from top to bottom doing a complete loop, but the majority just lay there and seemed to be going to sleep. Every now and then some would become restless and there would be some coming and going and occasionally an adult would start grooming, licking its back legs and abdomen most carefully. We counted sixteen, but there may have been more in the grass behind the mound.

At 7.0 all seemed to be asleep again, but by 7.10, when the light was beginning to go, there was a stir, six of them disappearing down one of the entrances. Most of the others edged nearer to this hole and appeared as a dark mass in the fading light. By 7.20 there was a general move into the den leaving one adult which was loath to go in. The light had almost gone when it finally retired.

This was very exciting! We had seen a lot for a first watch. At least sixteen were in the pack and all ages seemed to be present from the tiny young not more than a month or so old (which had bands that were just visible) through juveniles to adults.

We waited for a while, started the engine and got away, hoping the noise wouldn't frighten them too much. We thought we should watch again in the morning because if they had been frightened too much they would probably go off and abandon the den. We did at least know that they were there now and should make the best of our chances. It was a bit of a gamble but might at least provide a photograph.

We got up at 5.45 and after a cup of tea drove to the den and were in position by 6.30. There was a little light in the east but bats were still flying and a nightjar was churring away. The dawn chorus was interesting to listen to as we waited for the bandeds to wake up. The nightjar soon stopped its vibrant trilling and we saw it against the eastern sky as it flew off. We ate bananas in lieu of breakfast as we waited. Time went on but we saw no signs of mongooses, but in one way this was useful as the intensity of the light was improving all the time for photography.

At 8 o'clock, as if called by the alarm, the first mongoose appeared at the lower entrance. It was very suspicious! It looked straight at us, then moved its head up and down as it scented the air. We wondered whether it would ever come out, it was so hesitant, but after about ten minutes it cautiously emerged. Then the mound seemed to erupt as

31. Lions resting in a ficus tree at Ishasha
32. Lion showing aggression when disturbed while courting

33. Giant forest hog at Ishasha
34. Rousette fruit bats in a cave in the Maramagambo Forest

35. Thonningia flowers from the forest floor
36. Olive baboons at the edge of the Maramagambo Forest

37. A butterfly uses another as a resting place

38. The yellow pansy: a common forest butterfly

more and more appeared from the same hole. Each one looked straight at us before climbing on the mound and going off; there was no waiting around. We got some pictures as they were emerging and counted them as they went off into the long grass and disappeared. There were twenty-three in all, including four very small ones.

They had obviously been most suspicious of us and we thought it unlikely that we should see them again; however, nothing had harmed them and most animals get used to vehicles very quickly and take little notice of them, so perhaps we should be lucky and they would tolerate our presence. There was little chance of seeing them again until the evening anyway, so we went to Pelican Point to see the birds for a change. Most of the larger birds had already dispersed when we arrived as some Africans were fishing for lung fish in the shallows and had disturbed them, but we were interested to identify the long-toed lapwing, which was very similar to the commoner spurwing, except that the black patch went right round to the back of the head. Greenshanks were probing at the water's edge and a lesser egret was fishing close by.

We were anxious to get back to the mongoose den that evening to see their return, if in fact they hadn't deserted. We backed on to the same bush and had got nicely settled when an elephant came up to the back of our bush and was about to browse, but on sensing the presence of the Land-Rover a few yards away it decided we were not nice to know and lumbered off, tossing its trunk in irritation.

Six-thirty (the time the bandeds came back the previous night) came and went. Six forty-five, 7 o'clock – not a sign. We consoled ourselves by seeing how many birds we could identify from their songs as the evening chorus got under way.

Light was now going and a bushbuck quietly browsed in front of us quite unconcerned. If only mongooses would be equally co-operative! No sign at all! Before leaving we put more grass stems over the entrance in case they should come back after dark, but the odds seemed to be heavily against it as it certainly looked as if they had deserted.

For the next two days we left the area severely alone and concentrated on other projects, but when we did have another look we found one grass stem down but the others were as we had left them. It didn't look very promising, but there was just a chance that they had returned. We looked for fresh dung but we found it difficult to recognize any, bearing in mind the drying effect of the hot sun. We replaced the grass stems firmly, intending to visit again the next day. However, in the early evening we were stopped by friends who said they had just seen a pack of bandeds playing about a quarter of a mile from the den. This sounded as if they could be the same lot, and if so we might still have time to see them return if we hurried. To avoid disturbance we decided to watch from the opposite hillside and used binoculars. On arrival we could see no sign of them round the mound, but we waited hopefully. Gradually the light faded, but no bandeds came into sight. It looked as if, after all, they were using some alternative den not very far away. We left before it was quite dark intending to search carefully the next day for an alternative den.

The next morning we found no sign of another den anywhere, although we combed the area most carefully; however the grass stems were again knocked down from one entrance in the old mound and it certainly looked as if it had been visited. The ground was very dry, but we did find tracks of bandeds just visible in the dusty surface. Had they returned after dark the night before? Obviously we had to watch once more and make quite certain. At all costs we must not disturb them if they were there, so once more we watched from the opposite hillside.

We were full of hope to begin with, but as time went by our mood began to change and it looked as if we were up against a blank wall once more. Then at 7 o'clock we saw one as it crossed an open patch between bushes a long way over towards the channel. It doubled back, and we lost it again. Not long after we saw another in the same place, then a group of seven others crossed the same open patch and disappeared behind bushes. We did not pick them up again until about a quarter of an hour later, by which time they were quite near to the mound. They looked very tired and four of them flopped down near a bush, but eight more climbed the mound and lay down just out of sight under the cover of a bush. Not long after, another group appeared and flopped down in the long grass with the others.

A Land-Rover passed along the track not very far away, making quite a noise and immediately several of them stood up like marmots, alert and listening. When it had gone they subsided once more into the long grass. At 7.25 there was a general movement and they clustered tightly in a mass round the two entrances as they had done when we first watched them. They had all disappeared inside by 7.33.

All very satisfactory! Presumably they had been using the den all the time, but had come back after dark and so escaped our notice. We had decided to concentrate our efforts on finding as many dens as possible, as we could then compare the behaviour of different packs. During the day we methodically searched other regions of the Park and in the mornings and evenings whenever possible we watched the original pack at what we now called Den 1.

One morning we were searching the rather open area at the back of the Nyamugasani Ranger Post when we came across a pack of about twenty bandeds. We turned the engine off and at once they all stopped, listening and watching – two stood up characteristically to get a better view. They did not wait long, but moved off in several groups and disappeared. We presumed the pack would reunite later, but how did they keep in touch with one another?

Coming back two hours later we saw them again in roughly the same area. Was there another den nearby? We looked most carefully, but found no sign at all. More mysteries!

We came across other packs in different areas, mainly during the mornings, but failed to find any more dens. Many hundreds of termite mounds were investigated closely and vast numbers of possible clumps of bushes examined. We looked for the characteristic patches of dung, but again no luck.

Meanwhile our morning and evening watches continued and we learnt a lot about the behaviour of this pack. At first we only observed them from the opposite hillside as we were afraid of disturbing them, but this had the advantage of our knowing that their behaviour would be quite natural.

In the evening we could never predict from which direction they would come when making their way home, except that they never came from below the den. It was always from left or right, or from over the hill top and down to the den. Presumably they had been foraging during the day in rather different areas each time. They came back at varying times, but their final retirement was almost invariably within a few minutes of 7.35. This was just as it was getting almost too dark for us to see, using 7× 50 binoculars. On one occasion we did not see them until 7.30. They came over the hill top at a fast pace in a long snakey line and went directly to the den and almost at once went inside. Two nights later, after a showery period, their behaviour was very different. We saw them first at about 7 o'clock, a big scattered group foraging as they came and investigating any likely spot for prey. They seemed to be in no hurry to get to the mound and we noticed on other occasions that they came back earlier after wet weather, presumably because food was easier to find when the ground was damp. There was certainly no flopping down and going to sleep on the way home as there had been when the weather was very hot and dry.

They were easily frightened. A sudden noise would cause them to run for the mound and if a fish eagle flew over they would run for cover or watch very carefully, ready to do so if it came nearer.

Morning watches were always interesting. The air was usually very still, especially after thundery rain the previous night. There was always plenty to watch while waiting for the bandeds to emerge from their den. We got to know the spurfowl in that area quite well as the cocks are very territorial and one bird would regularly climb a particular termite mound near where we parked the vehicle and make its typical single rasping note. After doing this repeatedly for some minutes it would fly down making more raucous noises before going off into the long grass to look for seeds. Clearly the vocalization was for the benefit of other cocks nearby, which answered in like fashion, as the hen took no notice of this performance but continued her search for food quite unconcerned.

The bandeds usually first appeared between 7.45 and 8.15. They were in no hurry to get up. At first they would cluster near to the mound, stretching and yawning. When they yawned the mouth opened extremely wide and you could see the red interior of their surprisingly large mouths. Some groomed, others went over the mound to the main defaecating area and returned a little later. There was a little play between juveniles, but it was not a conspicuous feature at this den. This was a time of leisure with plenty of coming and going in front of the den. After twenty minutes or so, one adult would go off into the long grass and others would follow, and soon the whole pack would fan out and start foraging as they slowly made their way along the contours of the hillside.

We had good chances of counting them accurately as they left. This pack contained twenty-three, of which four were very small, eight appeared to be juveniles and the remainder adults. We had no means of telling which were males and females.

We now felt we knew their general behaviour near the den fairly well, but somehow we had to watch from much nearer to see it in greater detail. We did not wish to repeat our previous attempts by parking a Land-Rover nearby as this had obviously disturbed them, but perhaps a hide could be erected?

A simple hide was easily made by stringing papyrus stems together to form a long mat. It could be rolled up for transport and erected by tying to posts. The only suitable site was where we had previously parked about thirty-five yards from the den, as the slope of the hill made it difficult to see the mound well from the other clumps of bushes. Ten yards away we found a place where we could leave the Land-Rover where it would be completely invisible to the mongooses. This gave us a sense of security if game should become too curious. We dragged a bough from a broken-down euphorbia in front of the hide to break up the outline and hoped the hide would not worry them too much. That evening we watched from a distance to see their reactions when they returned.

The weather was bad; there were heavy clouds about and thunder in the distance. We saw the first mongoose quite early, and soon the whole pack was slowly winding its way down the hill towards the den. They were still foraging and appeared to be in no particular hurry. By 6.50 they had reached an open area about ten yards from the den and about forty yards from the hide. Suddenly there was a mad rush for the den and all went in except five which wandered about for a bit before joining the others inside. What had disturbed them? Had they suddenly caught sight of the hide and panicked? We could see no other possible cause, but their reactions on emergence the next day should clinch the matter.

It was still just raining after a wet night when we got into position the next morning. An adult looked out at 8.07 but soon backed in again and we didn't see another until 8.35. This one was very suspicious and scented the air most carefully. It then came out of the left entrance, ran across and down into the right one. Another appeared almost immediately, looked in the direction of the hide, sniffed, ran across and also went into the other hole. This pattern of behaviour was repeated several times. If the animals were suspicious of an enemy nearby, then quick dashes from hole to hole might be the least hazardous method of testing the situation. On one occasion we did in fact see a leopard lying on top of a den and it would not have been visible to the mongooses until after they had emerged, so this type of hazard was a real one.

The main pack did not emerge until about 9.15, more than an hour later than usual. They soon went off and everything suggested that they were most suspicious of the hide and that its presence was unlikely to be tolerated, but we had to watch to make sure, so that evening we were back again. To our surprise we saw them quite early, but they did not actually come near the den until the last moment. Then about ten of them came in close together, head to tail like a long black snake in the failing light, but curiously another group still remained outside and did not appear to be worried, and they were still near the mound in the grass when it was too dark to see. Why the difference of behaviour in the two sets? They were certainly puzzling creatures!

We watched several times after this but never saw them again, so we had to conclude that the hide had been too much for their peace of mind and they had gone elsewhere.

For the next few days we redoubled our efforts to find new dens and tried to discover where the pack had gone to from Den 1. The hyaena den seemed to be a possible alternative as it was not too far from it but there were no fresh signs of occupation. We did in fact see a small group of them during the day in that area, but they appeared to be only passing through as the original holes were not used and no fresh dung appeared.

It was during this time that we collected a lot of dung samples from the region of Den 1. Much of this was analysed by Sandy Harcourt, a student working at the Unit. It was surprising to us that it contained so few categories of food, the most abundant being coleopterous. Many species of beetle were represented, but the greatest number were dung beetles, especially the smaller scarabs, but ground beetles were also present. The second most common remains were of the large millipedes, their ringed skeletal segments showing up in every scat examined. Obviously they were a most important item of diet during the period of the year that we studied them. Dung from Den 1 also contained a number of large cocoons of a species of ant, but little else was present.

We were lucky enough to watch them hunting for food on several occasions. Their typical behaviour was to fan out over the area looking all round them for possible sources of food and keeping their heads close to the ground as if using their sense of smell. They would investigate any tree stump which was rotting away, but they spent most of their time examining the piles of dung left by elephant or buffalo, especially the former. Each pile was torn to pieces with the front paws before putting their sharp noses into it to extract the prey. In this way the whole pack travelled slowly in a definite direction investigating any likely habitat for prey within its compass. If one found something to its liking its neighbour would often run over and investigate.

I have no doubt that their food is much more variable than appeared through dung analysis, but we found no fragments of bone, no skin or hair. If we had analysed stomach contents perhaps we should have found more of the softer prey which are almost completely digested – snails might come into this category.

From our limited investigation it was very clear that banded mongooses are greatly dependent upon the presence of the larger game, as it is their dung which attracts the dung beetles and millipedes. This is specially true of elephant dung which contains a great deal of semi-digested vegetation which provides food, moisture and shelter for the big millipedes. We wondered whether bandeds would exist at all if no large game was about.

When foraging, the members of the pack kept within easy seeing or hearing distance of each other and at the slightest alarm would either run for the shelter of a nearby bush, or, if caught in the open, bunch together or go into a line. Sometimes we disturbed a pack as it crossed one of the tracks. If we stopped at once and turned the engine off all those left behind on one side would race across to rejoin those which had already crossed; they nearly always followed in a line or parallel lines when doing this.

The bunching together was an interesting reaction which occurred when they were frightened by a predator and there were no bushes nearby for shelter. We saw this happen on several occasions when eagles flew near. Bunching presumably gives the impression to the aggressor of a single, much larger animal and makes attack more difficult. The combined biting power of over twenty mongooses close together must be formidable – quite enough to deter all but the largest predators.

We continued our search for dens by asking at each Ranger Post whether they had seen any mongooses and if they knew where they bred. Not much information was forthcoming, but at Katunguru the Ranger told us he had seen a pack very recently in the evening down by a creek. When he came on them, they had disappeared into the bushes, but as it was then nearly dusk it seemed likely that their den would be quite near. This creek, which joined the Kazinga Channel, was bounded by well-wooded slopes, euphorbia trees mainly with dense clumps of bushes and grassy patches between. At the Kazinga end the creek was quite deep and a school of hippos lazed about in the water, but inland it merged into a muddy marsh where a number of water-birds were feeding.

The Ranger showed us where he had seen the mongoose and we searched all round the area. We soon found piles of dung and not far away was a termite mound which had several holes in it of mongoose size. One hole appeared to have been freshly dug out, judging by the loose earth which was lying below it, and there was more fresh dung on top. We were certain this was another occupied den. About thirty yards from this den we found another old termite mound partly covered in vegetation and with seven holes in it. Dung was all over the place and a musky odour pervaded the whole area. The dung didn't look quite so fresh as the other, but the den had clearly been occupied very recently. This was a most heartening discovery!

Returning to the first den, a small dark brown animal moved quickly across an entrance following the course of one of the tunnels. It was only visible for a fraction of a second and we were not certain what it could have been. It might have been a young mongoose or perhaps some rodent exploring the den or even living in it. It would certainly be a stroke of luck if it was a baby mongoose.

We explored the terrain to find the best position for watching the two dens. It was not very easy to find a good place on the opposite hill-side as bushes constantly obscured the view, but we found one place where the open spaces round the dens could be seen easily enough, although one den was hidden by a euphorbia. We decided to watch from there that evening and wondered which of the two dens they would use.

To get the Land-Rover to the chosen spot we had to make a big detour as the creek made an impassable barrier, but it proved to be a good vantage point as we could view an immense area with binoculars and although most of it was fairly densely clothed with trees and bushes there were many open grassy spaces in between. It was our experience from watching Den 1 that the mongooses would cross these open places on their way home, so we should be able to see them at intervals as they travelled back.

At the Kazinga end of the creek some fishermen were cooking their supper on the shore prior to going out fishing in their canoes. They were singing and making quite a lot of noise when we arrived, but the mongooses were probably used to this, as we subsequently discovered that it happened most evenings.

We saw the pack first, far over near the top of the hill. They seemed very alert, constantly standing up as if listening to the fishermen far below them. We lost them behind bushes but about forty-five minutes later we made out two groups walking parallel to each other and now very much nearer the two dens. We counted eight adults and five juveniles in one group and nine adults and two juveniles in the other. Both lots eventually converged on an open space about ten yards from the second and larger of the dens we had discovered – now called Den 2. They lay about in characteristic attitudes doing a little grooming but otherwise completely relaxed. They all disappeared towards the old mound and out of sight at about 7.20. As far as we could tell, none went to the den with the newly excavated entrance (Den 3), but it was possible that they had approached it from the back, unseen.

At 7.30 the light was getting poor and we were putting the binoculars away before leaving, when to our astonishment – there, not ten yards from the Land-Rover was a banded mongoose standing up and looking at us intently. Another came out of the bushes to our right and more followed. We counted twelve as they ran across the open grass in front of the vehicle before disappearing into the bushes! They couldn't have been part of the same pack we had been watching, as the creek was between them and they were moving in the opposite direction. We concluded that there must be another den on this side of the creek. It couldn't be far away, as it was nearly dark when we saw them. This was something else to look for. Our luck seemed to be in.

We were unable to look for the den at once as we spent a few days in the Budongo Forest looking for chimpanzees, and at Murchison Falls National Park, but on our return we explored the area on foot. The Ranger told us there were four bull buffalo which frequented the area, but he described them as a peaceful lot. We hoped he was right, but kept a good eye open for them in case he wasn't!

Den 2 showed obvious signs of being occupied, with a lot of fresh dung nearby, but Den 3 had no fresh droppings and appeared not to have been used, so it seemed that the pack we had watched had all gone to Den 2.

We then went over to the opposite side of the creek, walking methodically towards the channel from the place where we had seen the second pack. We found one very old mound which might have been occupied at one time, but nothing else until we came to the edge of the Channel where there was a hippo erosion gully. Here we found a lot of fresh dung, and there, overlooking the water, was the den. It was not conspicuous from the landward side as the entrance faced the channel, but it was clearly being used. There were three main openings and we could see where the animals had worn the grass down when lying out. We thought we should watch for them later in the day and the best place seemed to be from the opposite side of the creek not far from where the fishermen had their canoes.

That evening we made an early start. The track was very dry and we disturbed a number of spurfowl who were having dust baths. Parties of guinea fowl were feeding busily in the more open spaces, looking like animated tea-cosies as they hurried away at our approach.

We used to see these attractive birds in the early morning and evening more often than at any other times.

Near to Katunguru a large troupe of vervet monkeys had their territory and in the early evening they were usually not far from the track. On this occasion we saw about thirty, with a bushbuck in attendance. They sat up and looked at us, very alert, and ready to run at any moment. Infants were being carried, clinging upside down to their mothers' bellies and when we stopped the majority ran to cover, but two or three large males lingered on appearing to act as guards.

It was a wonderful evening for watching when we reached the creek. The sun was brilliant behind us and the colours showed up beautifully. It was very hot and we envied the hippos lying in the water just below the mongoose den; they looked so peaceful and contented huddled together among the drifting Nile cabbage. An egret stood at the water's edge, stiff and vigilant, and an Egyptian goose watched the hippos as they yawned and snorted and made rude conversation. A ring-necked dove started its monotonous three-part song from a euphorbia nearby and a yellow-vented bulbul perched just above it, displaying the yellow at the base of its tail. Martins were hawking lake flies over the creek, but happily for our comfort there were not too many about.

We could see no mongooses, but this did not surprise us, as when we saw them last they had been very late in going home. Anyway, as there was always plenty to watch and listen to, time was unimportant.

A little bee-eater had its nest in the cliff face opposite, not far from the den. It kept making sorties over the channel to catch insects in the manner of a flycatcher, returning to a convenient perch each time. A large hippo yawned cavernously and I found myself yawning in sympathy. A pied kingfisher was still hovering over the water making repeated false dives before finally piercing the water and catching a fish. I wondered how many dives it would make during the course of a day before getting enough for its needs. The sun got lower and some of the birds started their evening songs. A white-browed robin chat mournfully descended the scale in semitones and a cock spurfowl gave its raucous territorial cry, but there was nothing to beat the wild stirring cries of the hadada ibis as they flew past on their way to their roosting sites.

It was all very lovely, but it would have been nice to see some bandeds! It was now 7.15 and the light was going; the colours, so brilliant half an hour before, had now become drab. The egret flew off –

pure white with black legs and beak – a wonderful contrast to the darkening waters. The spurfowl gave another volley of territorial fire from the top of a termite mound and there were wild cries from a fish eagle as it slowly made off to its roost. An elephant trumpeted somewhere behind us.

We strained our eyes through binoculars searching for brown shapes crossing the open space near the den – but nothing! Regretfully we packed up; it was too dark to see. What had happened? Just late home? Or had they deserted as a result of our visit? It was disappointing!

For the next fortnight things were pretty hectic. During the day we mainly searched for dens both by vehicle and on foot, and when the weather permitted we watched Dens 1 and 2 at Katunguru. The 5 March was a red-letter day as we decided to watch for the first time from a natural hide – a group of bushes about fifty yards from the den. It was a calculated risk as elephant and buffalo were about, but we thought it unlikely that we should be disturbed. We hoped the pack on returning would not come near enough to pick up our scent, but their behaviour was so variable we had to chance it.

We arrived at 6 o'clock and leaving the Land-Rover at the top of the hill, we cautiously approached the bushes which were to act as our hide. No sooner were we settled than we saw a tiny mongoose at one of the entrances. At last we had a good uninterrupted view and with binoculars could see every detail. The baby was soon joined by another; they were dark brown all over and certainly not more than five inches long, plus a short tail. The first adult to show itself was rather suspicious and when a spurfowl gave its raucous call it shot in again, followed by the babies, but they were not in for long. A little later another noise drove the babies in again but this time the mother, if that's who she was, stood up and listened intently. When the babies emerged and went to nuzzle her she seized one by the scruff, shook it roughly and threw it down one of the holes. The second was treated in a similar way; she was certainly exerting her parental authority, if she really was their mother.

The pack must have returned unseen from below the den, because at once there was great activity. Two adults and a juvenile climbed over the mound into view and a baby poked its head out of one hole to greet them; however, the mother made a lunge at it and it retreated. Then others arrived from the bushes behind and there was so much coming and going that it was impossible to keep track of individuals.

One adult that emerged from the mound was followed by a writhing mass of babies, certainly seven of them! Some were trying to suckle and were dragged along underneath her body when she moved to another part of the mound. The babies got little satisfaction from this and started to play together. They chased each other and jumped in the air, twisting as they did so; others wrestled face to face with their mouths locked together and shook each other violently.

There were further noises from a spurfowl and the young disappeared once more, leaving the adults on various parts of the mound. Then to our astonishment we saw a large black cobra coiling about in the grass to the right of the den. It reached the bottom and started to climb, investigating the entrances on that side. Here was drama! Were we going to witness a fight between this deadly snake and the mongooses? We held our breath, knowing the young were just inside and might pop out at any moment. At last one of the adults caught sight of the snake (it had probably been unsighted before) and immediately moved over towards it. It was a careful, wary approach, but there was no hesitation. A second adult went over the top of the mound and faced it from a different angle and we waited for the attack, but none came either by snake or mongoose. The cobra just slithered away and was lost to our sight. What an anti-climax! When we thought about it, it was obvious that if the cobra had put its head into the den it would have been killed quite easily, as it could not have turned round, and retreat was probably the best policy. But what would happen during the day? If the babies were left on their own they would be easy prey for a snake. We remembered the brown animal we had just glimpsed at Den 3 when we first discovered it. We were more than ever convinced that it must have been a young banded and as Den 3 had not been occupied since, the mother must have moved her family over to Den 2 after the disturbance caused by our first visit. Did an adult remain behind to guard them? We decided to have a long watch one day to see what happened.

It was now getting dark and at 7.30 there was suddenly a general movement of adults from the long grass to the mound. They had probably been there for some time, just out of sight in the open space where we had seen them previously from the opposite hillside. It was impossible to count them, but there must have been more than twenty clustering round the holes in a huddled mass. By 7.35 all but one had retired into the den, the last being an adult which lay across the bottom entrance as if there was no room left inside. When it was quite dark we got stiffly to our feet and crept quietly away, well satisfied.

The next morning we arrived at 7.20. One adult was already on the mound and it seemed very suspicious. It may have heard us as we crept towards the same bushes we had used as a hide the evening before, but it was more probable that it had got our scent, as the wind had changed since the previous night. Two other adults emerged and were equally suspicious; but they were not greatly alarmed and before long some juveniles joined them, followed by the babies. The latter were very active and jumped about with lightning-quick movements, but the mother appeared to dislike having the babies outside and reacted as we had seen the previous evening by taking one by the scruff and literally throwing it down the hole and pouncing on another and pushing it roughly towards the nearest entrance. In spite of this treatment they kept reappearing and her efforts were largely unsuccessful.

Then came the main emergence of adults and juveniles and for a few minutes the mound seemed crowded with brown shapes before they slipped away into the grass and disappeared from sight. Andrew was watching from the opposite hillside and saw them go; they were foraging steadily as they left the area. The pack included fourteen adults and a number of juveniles of two sizes, some of which played together for some time before catching up with the rest.

Meanwhile the mother remained on the mound with a single juvenile, the babies being inside. She was still rather suspicious so we thought it best to leave, and choosing a moment when she was temporarily inside the mound we crept quietly away.

That evening we continued our observations, splitting up again so that this time Betty and Andrew went to the bush hide while Sandy Harcourt and I watched from the hillside opposite. Through binoculars we had some splendid views of their general behaviour as the pack came back early and spent a long time in an open space where we could observe them easily. It was interesting to see their reaction to a group of waterbuck which grazed their way slowly towards them. They watched intently as they came nearer, standing up for long periods at a time and only jumping to cover when they got within a few feet of them. One buck passed very near the den, but this caused no panic, they just quietly retired down the holes, emerging a minute or so later when they had passed.

There was a great deal of play on this occasion, possibly because they had returned rather early. Juveniles chased each other in circles and had mock fights, tossing each other violently as they wrestled together; but it was not only the juveniles. Two adults caught our attention particularly as they chased each other all over the place. After one of these bouts of chasing they stopped and faced each other, standing up and sparring together before continuing the chase, this time in tight circles; this led to mating. After separation there was another chase and a further mounting, and this pattern was repeated three or four times. The final mating lasted over ten minutes. All this time another adult was in close attendance, watching and partly joining in the play. This one mounted the same female for a prolonged mating after the first male had ceased. From this and other evidence obtained later it was clear that the species is promiscuous. We saw another bout of mating before the pack eventually reached the mound. The mating position was dog-like, the male grasping the female round the middle of her body. There was no neck biting, but he kept touching her neck with his open mouth. Before we left to rejoin the others, we again saw mongooses just in front of the Land-Rover. One after the other, they paused when they saw the vehicle, then ran across the open space, had another good look at us and then disappeared in the bushes. We were able to count twenty-one including juveniles. Once more it was nearly dark and they were obviously hurrying to their channel-side den. It was good to know they were still there, presumably they must have returned after dark when we watched for them previously.

Meanwhile Betty and Andrew from their viewpoint much nearer the mound also had a most interesting time. When they arrived they had seen eight babies for certain and one adult was with them. They all tried to suckle, but only two or three succeeded for a short time. The babies were active and when one wandered too far the mother retrieved it in her mouth like a cat with a kitten. Suddenly the mother stood up alert and listening, and a moment afterwards some of the pack returned. Two adults came right up to the den and were greeted, face close to face, by the mother and babies. This seemed to be a recognition ceremony. The adults disappeared into the den for a moment but on reappearing all three suckled. This was extremely interesting, as all three must be mothers but only one had looked after the babies during the day! They suckled for about seven minutes, but it was impossible to tell which babies belonged to which mother as there was so much to-ing and fro-ing between them. At one time two mothers had four each, at other times they were more evenly distributed between them. It was now certain that there were eight babies between three mothers. Some were slightly larger, but not enough to be sure that they belonged to a particular litter.

Further observations on another occasion confirmed that only one mother looked after the babies during the day and they definitely adopted the crèche system. Unfortunately we were never able to prove that the mothers took it in turns on different days to act as nannies, but it is obvious because of feeding problems that this must happen.

A few days later I was caught in a heavy thunderstorm while watching the mother and babies, and returned to Mweya earlier than usual. By the time I reached the hyaena den the rain had cleared, so I thought I would glance through binoculars at Den 1 to make sure that the sticks were still in position across the entrance holes. They were, but to my astonishment there was a leopard lying on top of the den! It is likely that leopards would kill bandeds, though I know of no actual case, but I was told of an incident where a lioness was seen to attack a mongoose which came rather near. It killed it immediately with a blow of the paw, but didn't take the trouble to eat it, and moved off.

Den 1 had now been deserted for three or four weeks and it seemed unlikely that it would be re-tenanted, so we decided to excavate it to see its structure. This would obviously be a strenuous business as termite mounds are notoriously hard, but we were fortunate to enlist the help of two willing members of the Unit's staff. First we stuffed newspapers down the tunnels so that loose earth would not fall in, and then took away vertical slices in succession, working from the front. Knowing what a large pack could get inside, I expected to find tunnels leading from a central chamber into the ground, possibly for long distances, but we found none.

The mound was 7′ in diameter and 3′ 8″ high measured from the front. There were three entrances leading to tunnels several feet long which converged on a central chamber 5′ × 3′ and 20″ high in the centre. One entrance tunnel gave off a side branch ending in a small chamber in which we found a few scats, and there was a rather larger off-shoot from a second tunnel which communicated with the main chamber. No termites were using the mound now, but we found the nest of a large species of ant in the upper part of it, and in it were many cocoons. We recognized them at once as the same sacs we had found when analysing the dung of this colony.

The floor of the central chamber was flattened and dusty and no 'bedding' of any kind was found, although we knew it had been a breeding den. Powdered remnants of old dried scats formed the dust on the floor. The walls were smooth and lighter in colour and appeared to be the outside of the original termite nest. It seemed incredible that no less than twenty-three animals had crammed into this restricted space each night during the two or three months of its occupation. No wonder they were loath to retire for the night!

We had now found three dens in all, but we wanted to find as many more as possible to see if this species showed any preference for a particular kind of habitat. On several occasions during our search for dens we had the help of the Park hunter. As he was armed, this enabled us to search more systematically, as we could comb the area on foot. Four or five of us would form a line about twenty yards apart and slowly move forward, examining each termite mound for dung, and holes of the right size. The hunter was usually somewhere in the centre of the line. In this way we covered considerable areas, but it was very hot work in the broiling sun.

It was interesting to see how he coped with the bigger game. The thing to do, of course, was to see them before they saw you! If a lone buffalo was seen, the hunter would show himself and clap his hands. The bull would get up, sniff and peer in our direction, probably too short-sighted to see us clearly, and then would lumber off. No trouble at all! Perhaps the method works best when there is a rifle handy! The danger, of course, is when you come on an old bull which is resting behind a bush or in some gully and you surprise it. Its natural reaction is to charge, and this can be extremely dangerous.

Going on foot was far better than by vehicle as it was much more thorough and you could go to many places where it was impossible to drive a Land-Rover. You could advance slowly, making hardly a sound, and if you walked up wind you had a good chance of seeing things before they saw you. While investigating the area between the main Park Track and Lake Edward we saw a pack of mongooses working on the bank at the edge of the lake. At first they were quite unaware of our presence and we got excellent views of their foraging behaviour.

Although we found dens in this way which had obviously been occupied, the remains of the scats were broken and dry and no mongooses had used them very recently. As we got more experienced, we realized that we would waste less time in searching, if we concentrated on regions where we had seen a pack either before 9 o'clock in the morning or after 6 o'clock at night, as presumably they were near their dens at these times.

The presence of considerable quantities of dung was nearly always a sign that a den was nearby, but several times we found collections where no dens could be discovered although we searched every possible place.

39. Encounter on the mountain road through the Impenetrable Forest

40. View from the Ruwenzori looking west towards the Ituri Forest

41. Banded mongoose pack on the move

42. Banded mongoose pack

43. Banded mongoose suckling young at the den

44. Banded mongoose tracks in mud

We concluded that these were just feeding areas, or places where a pack had rested during the day.

In the end we found ten dens of which five were old ones and from these we deduced that bandeds have a marked preference for old termite mounds, in fact only one was in a gully. All had bushy vegetation, either on the mound or very near it, which gave the animals adequate cover; they were never isolated mounds, but in places where game would not rub against them or trample on them; they were on a slope from which good views could be obtained, and all were within a short distance of a good water supply. They seemed to favour the areas near the channel or the edge of Lake Edward.

Every day now we watched Den 2 whenever we could, and occasionally watched the pack on the other side of the creek go back to their channel-side den (Den 4). The latter were always on the late side when returning, seldom appearing before 7.15.

We were anxious to find out how long the babies would remain behind at Den 2 when the pack went off foraging. They were growing fast and it was interesting to study their changing behaviour. One day I decided to have an extended watch of five or six hours to see what they did over the whole period and if the wind was right watch from a nearer vantage point. There were two other possible bushes which might act as hides and although they formed poor screens I thought they were worth trying. The idea was to go to the original bush hide at fifty yards to begin with, and while the animals were inside the den make my way to the nearer bushes and perhaps try for some photos. I went alone to reduce chances of discovery.

I arrived soon after lunch-time to find a baby was on the mound. Fortunately the wind was completely right and when the mother who was acting as nanny emerged she showed no suspicion. She lay down on her side by an entrance and the babies crawled on top of her. A few minutes later they all went in, so I took the chance to go to the nearest bush. It happened to be the better choice, as I realized later when Betty found the shed skin of a cobra in the other one. Presumably, that was where the snake lived – the one which I had previously seen at the den!

I had just set up the camera and settled in when the mother reappeared with all eight babies. It was exciting to see them so close as they played and clambered over the mound. Periodically they lay down near to the adult, keeping their mouths wide open, presumably as a cooling device. It was certainly a very hot day.

A kite flew low over the mound, but the mother, although vigilant, did not move; however some of the babies crept under her. When the danger was past there was more vigorous play and one baby turned a complete somersault as it slipped down the mound.

Play over, the babies huddled together near their nanny and I watched her cleaning them one by one. Taking one by the scruff, she put it down on the ground head first in front of her and vigorously licked it from back of neck to tail and turning it over she did the same for the under-side. This female had a pink button of a nose and the pale under-side of her chin showed up clearly as she groomed the babies. Some of them had crawled right under her and it was amusing to see a tiny face poke out and produce a vast red yawn.

Two of the babies clambered over her and kept tickling her chin which caused her to scratch violently. Then all the babies joined in the fun, jumping, climbing, chasing and running like mice between her legs. When she stood up at least six got right under her and one climbed on her neck, but she nodded her head so that it fell off. It tried again and succeeded in hanging on for a while until she moved away. Photography was not easy as their movements were so quick, but I was able to get a useful series.

When evening came the babies became more venturesome and explored the mound extensively. If one went into a hole the rest would follow, if one climbed the mound, the others would imitate. They could now run very fast, but if they strayed too far the mother would retrieve them. At various times some of the babies tried to reach up to her mouth as if to lick it, but I saw no sign of her regurgitating food for them, although they were probably old enough to be weaned.

It was about 6.30 when suddenly the whole pack returned with a rush, appearing like magic out of the vegetation behind the den. There was great excitement and I managed to count eleven adults on the mound at one time, but it was difficult to be certain of numbers as they were going in and out of holes and moving here, there and everywhere. After the initial exploratory and greeting behaviour they began to settle down and one mother suckled three of the babies for six minutes on end. Some of the adults started mutual grooming with their mouths or scratched themselves with a back leg like miniature badgers. There was some violent play between juveniles, leap-frogging, somersaulting and wrestling, mouth locked to mouth. Occasionally one animal would rush at the neck of another and be flung sideways by the movement of the other's head. Most of the play was a form of mock fighting and was accompanied by low but excited noises.

Some of the adults soon disappeared again into the long grass, leaving mainly babies and juveniles on the mound, but then a second mother started to suckle. She was in a half standing position with her front legs slightly apart; some babies were under her, others to her side, one lay on its back feeding lustily. Then another mother appeared and several of the babies went over to her for nourishment.

Adults were all the time going to and fro, but the majority were just out of sight in the long grass. Suddenly, four stood upright and looked to their right. I followed their glance and there were four male kob quite close. They must have seen my head move as they bolted immediately, but the bandeds looked on without taking fright.

At the usual time – about 7.15 – there was a general movement of animals back to the mound. What a crowd! They seemed to be everywhere – probably thirty-two in all. A quarter of an hour later most of them had retired for the night, so when darkness fell I carefully collected my equipment and went back to the Land-Rover. It was good to move my limbs after over five hours in that bush!

For the next four days we saw no sign of them. They had departed just when we had got to know them so well. We searched high and low for other dens in that district, but with no success. Had we scared them away? There was no way of telling, but I didn't think so. Their behaviour the last time I had watched had been comparatively free from suspicion. Perhaps the babies had been big enough to go with the pack and that was the time for a change of den. Their absence was a chance to examine the den carefully. We put tiny sticks over all the entrances, just in case; collected more dung for analysis; took photos of the den and regretfully wrote them off.

We still had the pack on the far side of the creek (Den 4) to watch, which was a small consolation, but unfortunately this pack had no babies in the den and it was very difficult to get near enough to watch them well. After watching this pack go off one morning, I made a routine check of the deserted Den 2 and to my surprise and delight found the sticks down. What was more, there was fresh dung nearby and three of the entrances had been cleaned out, judging by the fresh earth outside them. It seemed certain that they were back.

There were many questions to answer. Was it the same pack, or had another lot taken advantage of a vacant and desirable residence? If it was the same pack, had they all returned or had they split up now that it was so large? The babies presumably were now old enough to travel with the pack and this might well be the natural time for a pack to split. Of course we had to watch that night.

Elephants were a nuisance that evening as quite a number came to the creek and when they came our side they undoubtedly picked up our scent and this seemed to have set them trumpeting. As we were in the bush hide we had to keep a wary eye on them, but fortunately they decided to let us well alone.

As luck would have it, we didn't see a banded until 7.15 when the light was already beginning to go. Four adults were the first to arrive and they appeared to be very suspicious, but soon afterwards a larger group returned and we counted four babies among them. With all the coming and going it was quite impossible to estimate their numbers accurately and we were no nearer to knowing whether in fact the pack had split up. There was no play to speak of and they all went inside the mound by late dusk. It was excellent to have them back again, but we hadn't learnt the answers to our questions.

The next evening we tried again, but their behaviour was very similar, with another late return, and again we were unable to count them accurately. The only point of interest during that watch was the pack across the creek which we saw returning much earlier than usual. We could just see them from our bush hide. A party of vervet monkeys were playing on the opposite slope when the mongooses came into view and we wondered what their reactions would be. The mongooses saw them at once and approached cautiously but steadily along two parallel lines in the direct route towards their den. When they got to within a few yards the monkeys turned round and fled!

What turned out to be our last observations on the main pack from Den 2 was undoubtedly the most rewarding from several points of view. It was a morning watch and as it happened I was on my own.

Six or seven adults came out of the den soon after my arrival at the usual bush hide; they appeared very suspicious, but not of me. They were all looking to their left and kept scenting with their heads going up and down characteristically. I heard some fishermen in that direction and assumed that they were the cause. When four of the babies came out, behaviour was much as usual.

I thought I would get prepared for a colour picture if the light was good enough and they happened to come in my direction on their way off as I had previously had little chance of really close-up pictures of the pack.

At about 8.30 a group of adults and juveniles went off purposefully and disappeared and I thought they had gone for the day, but something must have disturbed them, and a few minutes later they came back to the mound. One mother had a cluster of babies round her; they crept under her chest and remained there with their heads poking out.

At 8.50 there was a general exodus and to my joy they took a route which would pass fairly close to my bush. Some did pass within about eight yards and either saw or smelt me, as they stood up and made their 'urrr' 'urr' noises which I had heard previously. There was a continuous low murmuring between them. I managed to get a picture of a few of them as they passed, but the click of the shutter frightened them and they scattered into the bushes. However, more followed, and one large adult male got level with me, stood up and made loud and urgent 'urrr' 'urr' noises and all the others stopped and listened. It kept doing this, standing bolt upright all the time for what seemed to be minutes. I was only partially obscured by the bush and it could obviously see me plainly, so I 'froze', but I was in a most cramped position, half lying on the ground, and I wished it would move on. When it did I slowly twisted myself round and saw that the pack was grouped about ten yards away on open ground in front of dense bushes. This was a wonderful place for photography, but all sorts of grasses and vegetation were in my way as I was lying on the ground. I took some shots all the same and at each click they all looked in my direction, but they were not too frightened; some went into the bushes, but they reappeared quite quickly. At last I managed to get to my knees without frightening them and this gave me a better viewpoint and I was able to get some better shots. At one point they all panicked and disappeared into the bushes each making its 'urrr' 'urr' noises at once, to give an almost explosive effect.

I thought they had gone for good, but took the chance of standing up and changing my camera to one with black and white film and had just finished when to my delight I saw a head poking out of the bushes, then another and another. Soon the whole pack was out as before. They were obviously torn between conflicting emotions of curiosity and fear, but fortunately curiosity seemed to be dominant most of the time. Eventually they got used to the shutter's noise and appeared to have forgotten that I was there. Some licked themselves, others bit at their fur, or scratched, using their hind legs. One dug a pit in the ground and put its pointed snout into it to eat something. (Afterwards I found the conical hole it had made and ants were still crawling in it.) There was quite a lot of boisterous play between juveniles but I was surprised when one adult mounted another and remained in the mating position for several minutes.

I counted eighteen at one time, but I was sure I was not seeing the whole pack but merely a large part of it. It looked almost certain that there had been a split. At last they decided to leave, going off in a leisurely way towards the upper end of the creek. However, three remained behind, and two of these mated once more while the third looked on, then they hurried after the main pack and away.

It was wonderful to have seen them at such close quarters for a period of nearly an hour and get what was probably the first photographic record of their most characteristic attitudes and behaviour.

We never saw that pack again! They may have been tired of my attentions, or perhaps it was just time to move on now that the young were big enough to travel with the pack. It was impossible to tell, but as our own time for leaving was nearly upon us we had fewer regrets. They had certainly co-operated magnificently!

CHAPTER SEVEN

Inter-Relationships of the Savannah

The more you study the ecology of an area the more you realize the complexity of the relationships between the plants and animals living there. It is only by painstaking research over long periods that some of these relationships are made clear. Not nearly enough research has been carried out to draw more than tentative conclusions, but nevertheless a general picture is beginning to emerge of the part played by some species in the life of the savannah.

The savannah in Queen Elizabeth National Park is no haphazard collection of plants and animals, but a most complex product of many interacting factors. These factors themselves are subject to considerable fluctuations and so the equilibrium resulting from their interactions shifts as the pressures increase or decrease.

The savannah, like any ecosystem, is made up of a characteristic flora, the primary producers of food for the whole complex; on these a host of vegetarian animals depend. Many of them are small, like grasshoppers; others immense, such as the elephants and buffaloes. There are also strong links between the carnivores and these vegetarians at all levels, whether they are lions feeding on buffalo, banded mongooses on beetles, or cattle egrets on grasshoppers. Scavengers, such as vultures or hyaenas, also play their part, feeding on the remains of the dead animals, while others such as scarab beetles feed on their dung. The dead remains of plants provide food for another group of which termites and millipedes are examples, and finally there are the parasites which are dependent upon most of the other organisms which make up the savannah complex.

These relationships are far from rigid. Many of the species have their preference foods, but they switch from one to another as circumstances dictate. There is enormous flexibility in an ecosystem as complex as savannah; if this were not so it would never have survived the fluctuations which have occurred during the past few million years.

It is easy to appreciate the dependence of one species on another in terms of food supply, but it is not always so obvious that this is a two-way relationship. The buffalo may be essential to the lion as a major source of food, but lions also benefit the buffalo herds by keeping the numbers down and weeding out the less fit. It is this two-way relationship, between predator and prey and prey and predator, between herbivore and flora and flora and herbivore, between parasite and host and host and parasite, that has resulted in the evolution of such a complex assemblage. However, to describe these relationships as two-way is to simplify the concept far too much, as in fact the relationships are multiple, each species having influence on and being influenced by a number of other species both directly and indirectly.

In some parts of Africa, savannah has been a fairly stable condition for many millions of years, but in Queen Elizabeth National Park there is little doubt that the savannah is not a climax community, and if left alone by man would soon turn into thicket and woodland with a consequent reduction in grazing and change in the characteristic fauna.

There are several important factors which tend to keep savannah in a fairly stable state. Because savannah is basically grassland, anything that favours the growth of grasses more than other forms of vegetation favours the maintenance of savannah. Of these factors, climate, fire and the effect of the large herbivores are very important.

The climate favours grasses because there are two wet seasons, March to May and August to November, and during the drier periods between there may be little rain for many weeks and the land becomes scorched. Not many plants survive these alternations, but grass can withstand drought as its fibrous root system penetrates to a considerable depth and top growth is quick when the rains return.

Similarly it is well adapted to withstand the fires which, when the vegetation is dry, sweep across the savannah and destroy the overground portions; however, the grass roots survive and new growth comes with the rains.

Grasses can also take great punishment from the large herbivores both in terms of constant trampling and thorough grazing. Even though they may be cropped almost to ground level the bases of the leaves continue to grow, as unlike the majority of plants their growing points are not at the tips. They also reproduce very effectively by vegetative means either just above or below the ground.

Thus grasses are well adapted to cope with these factors. In the case of fire there is the additional point that it helps to eliminate competition from other forms of vegetation, especially by preventing the encroachment of thicket and woodland by killing off the bushes and young trees. For this reason man has deliberately used periodic firing as a conservation measure: it preserves the grazing outside the national parks for the benefit of his cattle, and within its boundaries it ensures a continuing provision of food for the large herbivores. In the Park, the savannah is by no means uniform although it is basically of the short grass type. Most typically it forms vistas of open rolling plains with few trees or clumps of thicket to break up the uniformity. This type of savannah provides excellent grazing for many of the large herbivores.

Where the soil has become more eroded, as in the neighbourhood of the Kazinga Channel or Hippo Pool, due largely to over-grazing by hippos, dense thicket has sprung up. One reason for this is that fire has been unable to reach the young plants and, in the case of *Capparis*, being well equipped with spines, they have also avoided destruction by grazing.

Taken a step farther, the savannah soon turns into semi-deciduous thicket where bushes predominate and euphorbia trees make their appearance. Many of these dense clumps have their origins as isolated termite mounds. An active termite colony brings back great quantities of dead vegetation into the underground galleries which radiate from the mound. The rich soil resulting is a favourable place for germination, so it becomes colonized by termite-resisting plants of a shrubby nature. Due partly to termite activity and partly to trampling, the ground near the mound becomes bare of vegetation and acts as a natural firebreak, so the bushes survive and grow up into dense clumps. These bushes in their turn provide protection for euphorbia trees during their early stages of growth and when they grow large enough shade is produced to favour the growth of other species. These interactions are typical of the effects of one species on another and illustrate the complexity of the ecosystem as a whole.

Soil variation also affects the savannah. This is particularly obvious in low-lying areas where the soil is sticky and waterlogged for much of the time. Here the broad-leaved grass, *imperata*, grows in dense masses, but it provides poor grazing and most of the herbivores tend to avoid it.

Taking the African savannah as a whole, it is astonishing how many species of large herbivores are associated with it and how successfully they compete for the available food. In Queen Elizabeth Park there are fewer species than in most savannahs, but the number of individuals present is very large indeed. The absence of such species as zebra, giraffe and rhino is probably due more to recent historical events than to unsuitability of the area, but little evidence is available. Species which are present – elephant, buffalo, wart-hog and the various antelopes – are beautifully adapted to live in savannah country.

To live successfully in savannah a large herbivore must be able to cope successfully with predators, fire, periodic drought and seasonal variations in food supply. Great speed and endurance are characteristic of these animals, helping them to escape predators and fire and enabling them to travel long distances for water or food if supplies in one area give out. The elongated limbs and hooves of the antelopes are structural features which give them speed and dexterity. This need for speed is correlated with the relative absence of hiding places for the larger animals on the savannah. Wart-hogs are exceptional in having bolt-holes to run for if attacked and in these they are also safe from fire. Hippos find safety in the water and have less need for speed. Elephants, in spite of their huge size, are remarkably active and can move great distances at surprising speeds when the necessity arises.

The herbivores are also very well equipped with some organs which warn them of danger in time to use their speed to escape. The antelopes have excellent eyesight and with the eyes situated on the sides of the head they can scan all directions except directly behind without turning their heads. The large size of their external ears reflects the importance and acuteness of their hearing, and their ear movements help them to locate precisely the direction from which the sound comes. The sense of smell of antelopes is also well developed.

Elephants, buffaloes and wart-hogs have poorer eyesight, elephant and buffalo particularly being rather short-sighted, but they have compensation in their senses of smell and hearing, which are very acute.

The majority of the herbivores are social animals, going about in herds or family groups. This in itself is a protective pattern of behaviour as each individual benefits from the combined sensory awareness of the group; such behaviour is, of course, of special significance when young are with them.

For animals which rely largely on speed to escape from danger, the presence of young can be a great handicap, but the savannah herbivores have young which are remarkably well developed, and which can move almost as soon as they are born.

At first sight it seems extraordinary that so many species of large herbivores can exist in the one habitat without an intolerable degree of competition for the available food, but each species has its own ecological requirements, and although there is undoubtedly some overlapping, each does in fact have its own niche in the ecosystem. The different species are often very flexible in their feeding habits and so are able to make the best use of the resources at any one time of year, but they have their preferences and it is this selection that is an important factor enabling them to live together.

Elephants feed on a large variety of foods and are extremely adaptable, but when grasses are available in large quantities they are mainly grazers. They can tackle the roughest species which other herbivores cannot or will not touch, so easing the competition. In more bushy country they browse considerably and may break off large branches which they only partially strip of leaves, leaving unintentionally on the ground a lot of food for other herbivores, which otherwise would have been beyond their reach. By their destruction of trees, woody country may be converted into grassland, especially when in addition the area is fired; then more food becomes available for other grazers.

Another factor that separates one species from another is the proximity of water. Some are better adapted than others to withstand dry conditions. Buffaloes are grazers, but they have to drink regularly, so the herds are mainly found near the lakes or wallows. Waterbuck are antelopes which cannot withstand too much water loss and are never found far from water. They appear to have a preference for higher ground, where they get more breeze, or country where there is more shade, as here they can keep cooler.

Kob have a great preference for the red oat grass and seldom move very far from water. Although they stay together in considerable herds the males show strong territorial behaviour, using some locus such as a termite mound which acts as a marker. Mating occurs when females move into a male's territory.

Another factor which prevents competition among the browsers is their reach. In savannah where giraffes occur this becomes very obvious, but in Queen Elizabeth Park it is also true of such small antelopes as bush-duiker which browse near ground level, and bushbuck which feed higher up in the bushes. Both these species occur much more commonly in shrubby savannah than in the more open country.

The time of feeding also helps to prevent competition between species. Some, like the bush-duiker and the bushbuck, are largely nocturnal feeders; other species are more diurnal. In these ways the full productivity of the savannah is exploited and a great variety of species is able to live there.

Just as the herbivores have their particular place in the savannah, so the carnivores have their niches. Again there is much overlap in the food of different species, but nevertheless there are marked preferences. In Queen Elizabeth Park, the lions in the savannah round Mweya have an obvious preference for buffalo, but in the Ishasha region in the south their preference is for topi. When these are not available they will, of course, turn to any convenient alternative such as wart-hogs or buck. Lions are well adapted for this role and like all the cats they capture their prey by stealth. First there is the stalk, which may take a long time, and then the speedy rush and pounce. Members of a pride hunt together, but it is usually the females that do the actual attacking.

The other large cat in the Park is the leopard. With a strong preference for savannah with much bush or tree cover, it hunts by night for a variety of prey. Antelopes and baboons are commonly killed, but smaller prey such as hares and ground-nesting birds are taken quite often. The leopard is a solitary hunter and often waits for its prey to come near before pouncing.

Another member of the cat family is the serval – a medium-sized carnivore occupying a very different niche from the other two. Its prey is correspondingly smaller and includes hares and ground-nesting birds. Largely nocturnal, it hunts where grass is long and where the prey is picked up by the sounds it makes rather than by scent or sight, although, no doubt, scent plays some part. Its enormous ears help it to locate its prey, and when searching it moves with great care and precision, making no sound at all. Having calculated the position of its prey, it catches it by making a prodigious leap.

The last of this family is the African wild cat which is much the same size as the domestic tabby, but more greyish in colour. Hares, rodents and birds are their most usual prey, but unlike the serval they use their eyes much more and their movements can be very fast and bounding. Thus the four cats present in the Park show great variation in their method of hunting and their prey depends much on their size, the use of their senses and the type of country in which they hunt.

The largest member of the *Viverridae* is the spotted hyaena. It plays the dual role of scavenger and predator. Most of the available evidence suggests that in Queen Elizabeth Park it is largely a scavenger as regards the bigger prey, although large numbers of newly born young of the bigger herbivores are undoubtedly killed by them. They are most efficient scavengers as their enormously strong jaws can break bones which a lion cannot crack, and even after the vultures have picked the last morsels from them they can make a good meal of the polished remains.

Civets may also act as scavengers, which may account for their incidence close to human habitation, where they can keep a look out for scraps. However, the civet is also a predator in its own right and at certain times feeds largely on beetles, especially the larger scarabs, and the large millipedes. It is also somewhat omnivorous, taking fruits and berries when available.

Genets, by contrast to the civets, have short legs and hunt mainly by scent in the stealthy manner of a cat, with the body close to the ground. They climb very well and exploit the bird population which roosts in trees, although ground-roosting birds and various small mammals are also frequently taken.

The remaining viverrids found in the Park are the five species of mongoose. Virtually nothing is known about the niches that most of these occupy, but from our own observations it is evident that the banded mongoose largely exploits the presence of the big game, especially elephant and buffalo, by feeding on the dung beetles and millipedes which collect in their dung. Compared with the other species – the great grey, the black-tipped, the white-tailed and the marsh mongoose – it is adapted as a diurnal, mainly insectivorous carnivore. Hunting by pack seems to be a diurnal adaptation. There is safety in numbers if caught in the open by a potential predator, and the bunching together on these occasions is clearly an effective defence. Because the food consists of small animals, large distances may have to be covered to find enough, and foraging by pack is an effective method. Their reproductive behaviour is also correlated with social life. When the pack is large it is likely that several females will have litters at the same time and the young can be protected by a single mother while the pack is away feeding. In addition, the fact that any infant can suck any lactating female is another instance of division of labour within the social group which would appear to have an important survival value.

Finally, the ant bear must be mentioned as a carnivore which exploits the termite and ant populations, feeding almost exclusively on these insects. For this it is well adapted, having huge claws and powerful front limbs for digging and a tubular snout with long tongue for ingesting the insects. Its large, donkey-like ears give it early warning of danger, and it quickly can find a refuge in the huge underground chambers it digs with such ease.

I have made no attempt to outline the role of the birds, the reptiles, the insects and the host of other invertebrates which play a vital part in the savannah community. But perhaps enough has been said to hint at the complexity of this astonishing assemblage of inter-dependent organisms, each so admirably adapted to fill its niche in the African savannah.

Appendix

THE BANDED MONGOOSE: SUMMARY OF DATA

This species was studied over a period of nearly four months (late December 1968 to early April 1969).

THE DEN

Of the ten dens found, nine were in old termite mounds, the other consisting of burrows dug into an erosion gully. Five of the dens were in current use and five were old.

Of three dens known to be used for breeding, Den 1 was occupied for more than two months, Den 2 for over a month, and Den 3 was still in occupation when we left after six weeks.

CHOICE OF SITE

All dens had bushy vegetation either on the mounds or very near them. Nine of the ten sites were located on a slope that afforded clear views for some distance. All dens were within 300 m. of either the Kazinga Channel or Lake Edward and eight of the ten were within 75 m. of a good water supply.

STRUCTURE OF DEN

One breeding den (No. 1), which had been deserted for a month, was excavated. It was situated in an old termite mound with three entrances leading to tunnels 9.25 cm. in diameter which led distances of 210 cm., 135 cm., and 150 cm. respectively to a central chamber 157× 90 cm. in area and 50 cm. in height at the centre. There were two side tunnels ending in enlarged chambers big enough to house one or two animals or a family. No bedding was present and the floor was smooth and covered with broken fragments of millipede cuticle from the dung. Most of the dung was deposited outside the mound, but there was quite a number of scats in two of the tunnels and in a side chamber. No termites were present, but there was a nest of a species of large ant in a separate region above the main chamber. Cocoons of these ants were found in the dung of the occupying mongooses.

The number of entrances varied from den to den, but three was the minimum noted. In Den 2, there were seven holes of which five were constantly used, but usually there were preferred entrances. Smaller holes, too small for entrances, communicated with the interior and no doubt helped ventilation, but it is likely that these were originally excavated by termites.

THE SOCIAL UNIT

The largest number of individuals present in one den was 32 (Den 2) of which 17 were adults, 7 half grown juveniles, and 8 young too small to leave the den when counted. Twenty-three were living in Den 1 and 21 in Den 3. Both the other dens watched consistently contained juveniles, and one of them had very young ones just capable of going with the pack during the day. The number in the den was not necessarily the same as in the foraging packs. Evidence was obtained on one occasion of the occupants of Den 2 going off in two separate units and all returning in the evening. However, in the field, at least three packs had over 20 individuals for certain and, as it is often difficult to count all the animals due to the bushes and long grass, it is likely that many more of the packs seen were of this order.

FOOD AND FEEDING BEHAVIOUR

The food, as determined by dung analysis between January and March inclusively, contained remarkably few items. By far the most abundant food eaten was coleopterous, the beetle species present varying considerably but including many dung beetles. The second very common food was large millipedes, the skeletal segments of which showed up in every dung sample examined. The cocoons of a species of large ant were also consumed, but the contents were nearly always entirely digested. No mammalian hair or reptilian scales were seen in the dung analysed and no vegetable remains of any consequence.

The main occupation during the day was feeding. When the pack finally made off in the morning the animals all started foraging and whenever a pack was seen during the day they were always looking for food. The typical behaviour when undisturbed was to fan out over the area looking all round them for possible food, investigating each piece of dung left by elephant or buffalo especially, and tearing it to pieces with the front paws, picking out prey with their mouths. In this way the whole pack travelled slowly in a definite direction, with each individual investigating any likely habitat for prey within its compass. Young animals tended to keep near their mother, judging from instances observed near the den on leaving and returning. The members of the pack kept within easy seeing or hearing distance of each other and at the slightest alarm tended to bunch or go in a line. This was evident on crossing a road, when most of the pack followed each other in a linear manner.

DAILY ACTIVITY

(*a*) *In the Morning*

The average time of first emergence on eight occasions was 0.800 hrs., which was about an hour after dawn (range 07.20–08.15).

TABLE 1: Morning Activity

Date	*Den*	*Time of first emergence*	*Time of pack departure*	*Viewpoint*	*Comment*
5 Feb.	1	08.00	08.10	Near	Suspicious
12 Feb.	1	08.05	08.20	Distant	Unsuspicious
13 Feb.	1	Before 07.55	08.25	,,	,,
20 Feb.	1	07.47	08.20	,,	,,
21 Feb.	1	08.07	09.15	,,	Very suspicious of hide near den
6 Mar.	2	07.20	07.45	Near	Unsuspicious
20 Mar.	2	07.45	08.15	,,	,,
14 Mar.	3	08.15	08.35	Distant	,,

On finally leaving the area as a pack, the next few hours were presumably spent foraging. No pack was kept in view for long periods, but various foraging packs were met at different times of day. The great majority of sightings (23 out of 33) were between 09.15 and 11.30 hrs. Three were between 11.30 and 13.30, one in the late afternoon and six in the early evening between 17.00 and 18.30. Not much can be gathered from these data except that the animals were obviously active during the morning and early evening. It seems likely that early afternoon is a period of less activity, but less time was spent during this period in searching for them.

(*b*) *In the Evening*

Times of return to the den were again variable, ranging from 1½ hrs before dark to just after dark, but the times of actually retiring into the den were remarkably regular at 19.35 hrs + or − 5 min. (17 out of 21 times).

TABLE 2: Evening Activity

Date	*Den*	*Time of return to region of den*	*Time when all in*	*Viewpoint*	*Comment*
4 Feb.	1	18.35	19.30	Near	
8 Feb.	1	19.25	19.33	Distant	Suspicious
10 Feb.	1	19.10	19.35	,,	Unsuspicious
11 Feb.	1	19.32	19.35	,,	,,
14 Feb.	1	19.15	19.36	,,	,,
18 Feb.	1	18.50	19.21	,,	Low light intensity
20 Feb.	1	18.45	18.52	,,	Dark and thundery
21 Feb.	1	19.32	19.40	,,	Had been very suspicious of hide that morning
27 Feb.	2	19.20	19.35	,,	
3 Mar.	2	19.00	19.35	Near	
7 Mar.	2	19.10	19.35	Near and distant	
8 Mar.	2	18.20	18.45	Near	Heavy rain and dark
9 Mar.	2	18.10	19.35	,,	
10 Mar.	2	18.20	19.35	,,	
15 Mar.	2	19.20	19.43	,,	
18 Mar.	2	19.20	19.38	,,	
11 Mar.	3	19.30	19.40	Distant	Unsuspicious
12 Mar.	3	19.30	19.35	,,	,,
13 Mar.	3	19.25	19.30	,,	,,
18 Mar.	3	19.00	19.35	,,	,,
24 Mar.	3	19.15	19.35	,,	,,
25 Mar.	3	19.30	19.35	,,	,,

Note. There were no babies at Den 3, but there were at Den 2.

Much variation in behaviour occurred, some of which appeared to be correlated with (*a*) time of arrival in the vicinity of the den; (*b*) the presence of babies in the den; (*c*) the tiredness of the individual after a day's foraging; (*d*) suspicion; (*e*) the weather. Some of these factors were, of course, inter-related.

(*a*) Their behaviour when they returned early is typified by events on 20 February at Den 1. They came back slowly, foraging on the way. On reaching a bare area by some tree or bush within 18 metres of the den, they flopped down and rested. There was grooming and some play between the younger animals. Others stretched themselves full length on their bellies with front legs forward and hind legs stretched backwards. At about 19.15, when the light was beginning to go, they made a move towards the den and flopped down again. Some sprawled on the top and sides of the mound, others clustered in a mass at its foot. As it became darker, a few became restless and made towards the entrance until there was a cluster of animals round each hole. At 19.30 they started to go in and by 19.35, when almost too dark to see, the last one, an adult, retired.

(*b*) If young were in the den the pack usually returned early, but the majority would not approach the den at first. This group consisted of male and female adults, and their behaviour was usually as described under (*a*). However, the mothers of the young went at once to the den and suckled their offspring either on or very near one entrance down which they could bolt at any alarm. The mothers were accompanied by juveniles which by their behaviour appeared to be the young of the previous litter, e.g. they sometimes attempted to suckle too, but without success. The main group of adults returned as usual to the mound at about 19.15.

(*c*) Whenever the pack returned late, the animals appeared to be extremely tired. A late return was often correlated with hot dry weather. One pack at Den 1 got to within 50 metres of the den where they lay down and apparently went to sleep; a little later they made another move and lay down again. On reaching the den they went into a huddle and went to sleep once more, except for the odd individual grooming itself or making a slight movement. There was no play of any kind.

(*d*) When suspicious, they remained away from the den until the last moment, coming in with a rush when it was nearly dark. One day a papyrus hide was erected near Den 1 while the pack was away, but on returning in the evening the animals saw it at once and were very suspicious. The next morning they emerged late and each looked straight at the hide before going off. The following night they did not return until it was nearly dark; they approached very slowly and remained hidden by bushes until 19.32, when they were seen moving rapidly head to tail like a large black snake towards the den. Most of them went in at once, but a few remained near the entrance for a few more minutes.

(*e*) The effect of low light intensity and torrential rain caused them to return to the den early and retire inside.

RANGE OF ACTIVITY

This was not accurately assessed as no marking techniques were used. It appeared, however, that definite feeding areas were used by different packs. At Katunguru two packs were observed over several weeks. The dens were only about 400 metres apart, but they were separated by a creek containing water. Whenever the packs were observed homing they always came from their particular side of the creek as if the latter was the edge of their feeding territory.

It was known that two and possibly three different packs foraged over the peninsular area at Mweya, although no occupied dens were found in spite of systematic search over the area on foot and by Land-Rover.

PLAY

This was seen to occur much more in the evening, especially when they returned early and were not too tired. It was mainly between juveniles, apart from play of a sexual pattern prior to mating. Play was also very evident among the young which were nearly old enough to go with the pack.

At Den 2, play was first noticeable when the young, of which there were eight, were old enough to come out of the den and creep about it. This was an exploratory stage and they kept in close contact which seemed to stimulate play between them. They would climb, slip, turn somersaults and jockey each other for position, and this would initiate simple play patterns. They also played with the mother, climbing over and under her, and she would move off with several on her back until they usually dropped off. They would bite at each other's tails, probably because these moved within the line of vision.

Towards the end of the period prior to going off with the pack, play became very vigorous and the animals were amazingly versatile. Play would be accompanied by sharp little 'urrr-urr' noises and included somersaults, after which they would jump high in the air, twisting as they jumped; they also leapt over each other and chased one another in tight circles. Two would wrestle together, locked loosely by their open mouths. They would go for the fur on each other's necks and be flung off by a quick sideways movement of the head. Generally speaking it was mock fighting play.

REPRODUCTION

It is unlikely from observations made between late December and early April that there is a particular season for reproduction because during each of these months very young animals were seen with the pack and several sizes of immature animals were present in the same pack. Mating was also observed on 3 and 20 March, which, if fertile, would extend the period when young animals ran with the pack to the month of May and possibly June (gestation period is not known). However, it remains to be seen whether there are peaks for reproduction during the year.

The number of young per litter was not established with certainty, but in Den 2 there were eight young of roughly the same size being suckled by three mothers, and in Den 1 there were three young of the same size but suckling was not observed. Litter numbers were difficult to estimate as suckling was shared between any animals which were lactating. In Den 2, suckling was seen on many occasions. During the day one mother remained at the den while the pack went off and she was seen to suckle for short periods during the afternoon, but at 18.10 she suckled three young for six minutes on end. When the pack returned at 18.35, two females were greeted by the young and at once they too started to suckle. This continued on and off for at least ten minutes.

When a mother suckled she usually stood with her front legs stiff and slightly apart. The young crawled under her from the side or between her front legs. It was not unusual for a young one to lie on its back as it sucked. When three mothers were suckling at once there was a good deal of coming and going of the young and it was clear that they were not attached to any one mother.

When the young were nearly big enough to go with the pack, they were very active around the den. They played together vigorously and would keep climbing over the mother and climbing on to her back when she moved. At the slightest alarm they would bolt for an entrance and disappear, only to appear again a moment or so later. The mother would sometimes get them by the scruff, shake them and push them down a hole, but undeterred they would soon emerge again. On the final day before they all went off with the pack, two out of the three mothers remained behind to look after them; previously it had only been one.

It was not established how long the period was between time of birth and the time when they were big enough to leave with the pack for the day. However, their size on the day they left was approximately 14 cm. long including a 3·5 cm. tail (estimated from photographs including an entrance of known diameter). At this stage, they were uniformly dark brown and showed no sign of the banding.

Mating was seen first on 3 March. The pack at Den 2 returned to the area of the mound early but did not go direct to it. Instead they played for some time about 30 m. away. There was much play between juveniles and then adults were also seen playing together. This included much chasing and the standing up of two animals facing each other as if sparring together. One would then chase the other in tight circles and this led to mating for perhaps a minute. They then separated and another chase took place and mating occurred again. This pattern was repeated three or four times, the last mating being for nearly ten minutes. The position was dog-like, the male grasping the female round the middle of her body but finally bringing his front legs nearer to her hind legs. There was no neck biting, but the male kept touching her neck with his open mouth. Another male was watching all the time and mounted the same female for a prolonged mating after the first male had stopped. So it appears that they are promiscuous. It is likely that during a series of mountings only the last and prolonged one is effective.

TOILET BEHAVIOUR

Defaecation was seen to occur as a regular thing in the morning, after emergence from the den. Each animal would climb on to the top of the den or go to a bare place or mound nearby to defaecate. They were not observed to defaecate on returning in the evening. They dug no holes, nor scratched the ground, and the dung was scattered over a wide area near the den, but great concentrations were found in certain favourite places. The whole colony used the same area for weeks on end. The droppings were very easily recognized as those of banded mongoose by their concentration in one place and the obvious presence of millipede and beetle remains in them. The finding of droppings was a good clue to the whereabouts of the den. However, several areas were discovered where there were concentrations of fresh dung on a much smaller scale and these were not near any den that could be discovered. It is likely that these were in feeding areas and were used by day by the pack during its travels.

Grooming occurred commonly near the den. Scratching of the fur with a hind leg as in dogs was seen many times, the front paws being used very little except for cleaning the face. They would also lick their fur, but I saw no sign of them licking their paws to clean their face as in cats.

Mutual grooming between adults was noticed when they were lying in a close group on returning in the evening.

The mothers groomed the young constantly. The young animal lay down or was placed so that it was lying flat on the ground with its head almost under the mother's head. It was then licked repeatedly from behind the head right down the body to the tail. It was also turned over so that its ventral side could be cleaned too. This was most evident after bouts of suckling in the early evening.

Bibliography

Bere, Rennie, *The African Elephant* (London, 1966); *The Wild Mammals of Uganda* (London, 1962).

Carr, A., *The Land and Wildlife of Africa* (Time-Life International, 1964).

Cloudesley-Thompson, J. L., *The Zoology of Tropical Africa* (London, 1969).

Heller, E., *New Species of Rodents and Carnivores from Equatorial Africa* (Smithson misc. coll., 56 (1911), pp. 1-15).

Hinton, H. E., and Dunn, A. M. S., *Mongooses* (London, 1967).

Isemonger, R. M., *Snakes of Africa* (Books of Africa, Cape Town, 1968).

Maberley, C. T. A., *Animals of East Africa* (London, 1960).

Owen, D. F., *Animal Ecology in Tropical Africa* (London, 1966).

Spinage, C. A., 'Population Dynamics of the Uganda Defassa Waterbuck in the Queen Elizabeth National Park, Uganda', in *Journal of Animal Ecology*, vol. 39, no. 1 (1970), pp. 51-78.

Trustees of the Uganda National Parks (1965). *Uganda National Parks Handbook*, Kampala.

Williams, J. G., *A Field Guide to the Birds of East and Central Africa* (London, 1963); *A Field Guide to the National Parks of East Africa* (London, 1967).

Willock, C., *The Enormous Zoo* (London, 1964).